Al Trellis and P...

Building
with an
Attitude!

How to
analyze, understand,
improve, and enjoy
the home building business

Home Builder Press®
National Association of Home Builders
1201 15th Street, NW
Washington, DC 20005-2800
(800) 223-2665
www.builderbooks.com

Building With an Attitude: How to Analyze, Understand, Improve, and Enjoy the Home Building Business

ISBN 0-86718-482-5

Cover by David Rhodes, Art Director, Home Builder Press
Cover image copyright ©1999 PhotoDisc, Inc.
Printed in the United States of America

Library of Congress Cataloging in Publication Data

Trellis, Alan R.
    Building with an attitude: how to analyze, understand, improve, and enjoy the home building business / by Al Trellis and Paul Sharp.
            p.   cm
        ISBN 0-86718-482-5
1.   Construction Industry – Management. I. Sharp, Paul, 1946-   .
II. Title.
HD9715.A2698 1999   99-37234
                                                            CIP
690'.8'068—dc21

For more information, please contact:
        Home Builder Press®
        National Association of Home Builders
        1201 15th Street, NW
        Washington, DC 20005-2800
        (800) 223-2665http://www.nahb.com/builderbooks

Additional copies of this publication are available from Home Builder Press. NAHB members receive a 20 percent member discount on publications purchased through Home Builder Press. Quantity discounts also are available.

9/99 HBN/McNaughton & Gunn 2,000

Contents

The excerpts from **BUILDER** magazine are reprinted with the permission of Hanley-Wood, Inc.

The following essays originally appeared in Builder magazine in the column "Ask Al." *Get an Attitude*, Oct. 1998 p. 246. *The Semi-Custom Convergence*, March, 1999 p. 156. *The Search for the Magic Bullet*, April, 1999. *So, What's the Problem?* May, 1998 p. 234. *Set Yourself Apart*, July, 1996 p. 158. *Time for a change*, Dec.1996 p. 96. *Get Creative*, Oct. 1996 p. 200. *A Sense of Urgency*, June, 1998 p. 170. *Creating a Sense of Urgency*, July, 1998 p. 180. *Staying Focused*, Sept.1996 p.144. *Learning from your Mistakes*, Oct.1997 p. 224. *Crossing the Comfort Threshold*, May, 1999 p. 150. *The Power of Pricing*, Feb.1999 p. 146. *The Problem with Quality*, June, 1999 p. 160. *Is Anyone Listening?* Sept. 1997 p. 136. *Inform Your Clients*, Nov. 1996 p.130. *Positively Negative*, Nov. 1997 p. 130. *How to Deal with a Low-Ball Offer*, Jan. 1997 p. 324. *Celebrate your Success*, June, 1997 p. 164. *The 3 M's of Marketing*, Feb. 1998 p. 192. *Four Ways to Think About Price*, Feb. 1996 p. 162. *What Builders Want from Salespeople*, Dec. 1998 p. 108. *Profit Sensitive Compensation*, Jan. 1999. *Love at First Sight*, Aug. 1999. *Spec for Success*, March, 1998 p. 184. *Price Points, Product Mix and Lot Premiums*, March, 1997 p. 168. *Finding and Hiring Good People*, Jan. 1998 p. 302. *Collaborating for Success*, Jan. 1996 p. 342. *Who Killed Your Profits*, Sept. 1998 p. 162.

Acknowledgments

It's a truism that every book is the collective work of many people, who contribute their ideas, questions, and support. This is especially true of this book, which grew out of our experience as builders, as well as the consulting and speaking we've done for builders around the country. So we want to say thanks to the people who made this book and Home Builders Network possible.

All the state and local Home Builder Associations who have asked us to share our thoughts and ideas with their members.

Our corporate sponsors: Andersen Windows, Kohler, Subzero, and Corian. It's great to work with people who not only make a great product but also are trying to elevate the level of the building industry.

The many builders we work with, many of whom have won national recognition for their programs and achievements. To single out a few: Steve Klein, Brian Bailey, and Todd and Don Pohlig who were named America's Best Builders by *BUILDER* magazine.

Our thanks to peers and collaborators who have contributed ideas and insights, including Carol Smith, Steve Maltzman, and Jerry Gloss. Carol Hyman and Karen Kotowski of the NAHB Staff. The editors and staff at Home Builders Press. Bill Lee, our link to the building materials dealers, who distributes the *On the Level* newsletter through lumber dealers. Roberta Maynard, our editor at *BUILDER* magazine, and Boyce Thompson, the editor-in-chief.

Special thanks to Bill Watkins, our partner in HBN, and Al's partner for 25 years in the building business. Brad Trellis, our office manager, and Renny Trellis, who scanned the essays. Roselle Commins and Peggy Sharp, for putting up with us, and letting us rattle on about our ideas. And thanks to all the people who read our articles, attend our seminars, and participate in the learning process. Because of all these people, it certainly has been fun.

Book Preparation

Building with an Attitude: How to Understand, Improve, and Enjoy the Home Building Business was produced under the general direction of Tom Downs, NAHB Executive Vice President and CEO, in association with NAHB staff members James E Johnson, Jr., Staff Vice President, Information Services Division; Adrienne Ash, Assistant Staff Vice President, Publishing Services; Charlotte McKamy, Publisher; Kurt Lindblom, Acquisitions Editor and Project Manager; David Rhodes, Art Director and Production Manager; Erica Orloff, Copyeditor; and Elisa Subin, Production Editor.

Introduction

Success in the home building industry isn't just based on what you know, or what market you're in, or how lucky you are (although all those things can be important). To a large degree, success is an attitude, a way of looking at the world that enables a person to take advantage of the opportunities that come along, and to create those opportunities if they don't.

In 1991, Al Trellis, Bill Watkins, and Paul Sharp founded Home Builders Network to help builders through education and information. Our attitude was short and simple: "Building homes should be fun and profitable." Because if it isn't fun, and it isn't profitable, why would anyone be doing this? Building houses isn't easy. There are many easier ways to make money. But for most builders, it's both enjoyable and financially rewarding. When it stops being fun or profitable, it's either time to do something else, or change your operations and attitude so it's fun again.

Since 1993, Al has written a monthly column for *BUILDER* magazine, called "Ask Al." In 1996, Home Builders Network began a newsletter, called *On the Level*, which is distributed through lumber dealers across the United States. Many of the articles in this book are reprinted from these two sources. Bill and Al stopped building houses a few years ago, in order to concentrate on education and consulting opportunities. And we have to say that it's been challenging and fun. You learn a lot from other builders as you travel around the country and work with them to solve their problems and improve performance.

The insights from our writing, teaching, and consulting form the basis of this book. We hope that our attitude of fun and profit helps you develop a similar attitude, and that you find ideas here to assist you in improving your own business.

You Are Here!

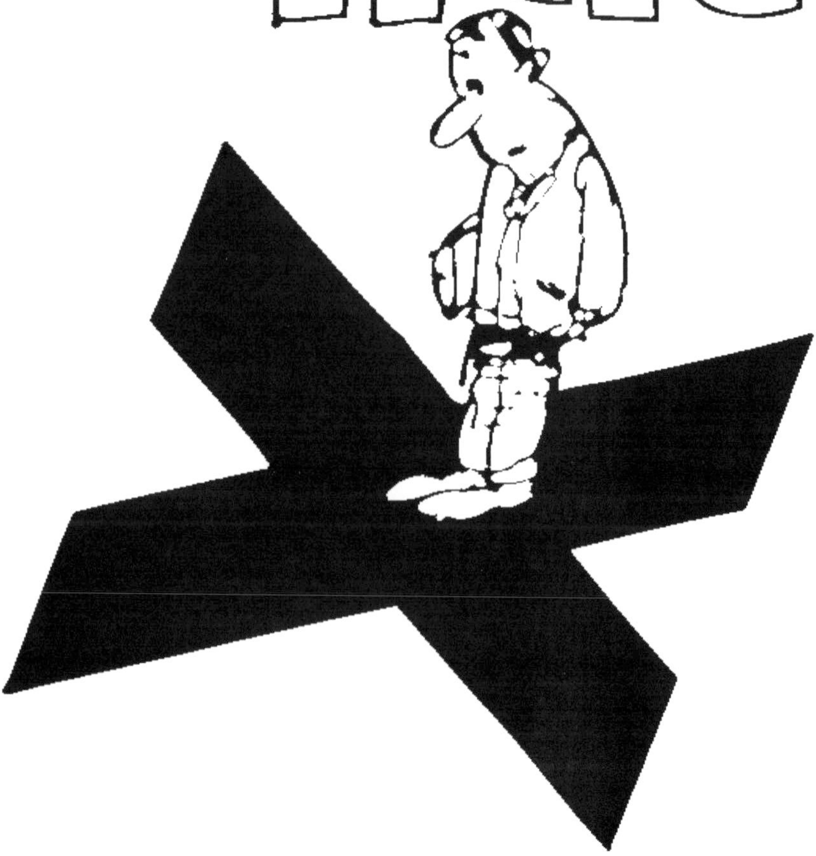

1
The Future's Not What It Used To Be

If your eyes and ears are open, you will realize that the home building business is rapidly changing. This isn't business as usual — since our industry is resistent to change. Tastes in housing styles and materials change slowly. But what is changing rapidly is consumer sophistication, management and communication technology, and the underlying economic structure of the industry. Bigger builders are buying up smaller builders to gain market share and greater access to capital markets. Buyers are shopping for homes and builders on the internet, and are more knowledgeable and demanding than ever before. New technology allows large sophisticated builders to extensively customize existing plans and compete directly with the custom building segment. Home design is increasingly important as a competitive element.

In the face of all these changes, builders have to build better and manage smarter than ever before. If you don't change, you'll simply be left behind, with a smaller market share and smaller profits. But change isn't easy. It requires thought, hard work and an open-minded attitude. But if you're willing to make the effort, it's worth it in terms of increased profits and productivity.

"The future is already here. It's just unevenly distributed."
— William Gibson

Get an Attitude!

When someone says you have an "attitude," they usually mean it in a negative way. Yet, not all attitudes are negative. In fact, having the right attitude is one of the most important factors in assuring success in business. And it's not just your workers' attitudes. Your own attitude greatly affects your entire operation. So, where do you fall in the attitude spectrum? Are you optimistic or pessimistic, open-minded or prejudiced, considerate or insensitive, cautious or risk seeking, aggressive or passive?

Your normal set of attitudes is an emotional blueprint for who you are, the way you view the world, and how you get things done. Think of your attitude as an emotional toolbox. You select the proper tools to help you solve different problems as they arise.

What's your frame of mind?

Builders can get into trouble when they limit themselves to always responding the same way regardless of the circumstances.

For example, optimism lets you keep moving when things get difficult. But that optimism must be tempered with a realistic assessment of the situation, allowing you to plan for when things go wrong. You can use aggression to protect your interests and to get things done. But too much aggression can lead to hostile work conditions and poor productivity. You use caution to avoid making fatal business mistakes. Too much caution, however, means you miss opportunities for success. Consideration allows you to work well with others and keep customers and workers satisfied. But too much consideration and you become a doormat. Open-mindedness encourages you to be receptive to new ideas. However, don't be so open-minded that you jump on every new fad that comes along or give up things that work just to try something new.

Check your profile

We often get along best with people who share a similar attitude profile. However, if you know you're lacking in one area, you may want to have people around you who can compensate for the deficit. So if you're often inconsiderate of others' feelings, you may need someone as a buffer between you and your customers. If you tend to be too risk-prone, you may want someone who errs on the side of caution to manage the financial controls.

Ask the right questions

In looking at your attitude profile, ask yourself, "Do I have the attitude tools I need to do the things I want to do? Am I using all my tools, or am I using the same ones over and over, regardless of the situation?" Always being aggressive, or always optimistic, is like trying to build a house using just a hammer.

Remember, attitudes are contagious. If you want your employees to have the right attitude, get the right attitude yourself.

"I don't have an attitude. I just want things done my way."

The Semi-Custom Convergence

In a world where the watchword is "Do it now," people don't have much patience for fence sitters. But sitting on the fence is sometimes the right place to be. It's the only place where the grass is equally green on both sides.

In home building, semi-custom building is the area where both production and custom builders seem to be converging. In a way, it makes sense for both. The production builder looks at the profit margins of the custom builder and says, "Boy, with those margins and our production skills, we could make a fortune." The custom builder looks at the volume of production builders and says, "Wouldn't it be great to build houses without buyers driving us nuts with constant changes?"

In reality, this drift toward the middle path is inevitable. Both the custom builder and the production builder gain significant advantages by shifting their focus to incorporate the best of the other's way of doing business. It's a little like buying a suit. Very few men want a suit right off the rack, without any alterations. Yet very few people can afford to buy a suit custom-tailored from scratch. Most of us find a quality suit we like, and then have it tailored to fit our measurements. We get the fit of a custom suit, at the cost of a mass-produced product.

Custom builder advantages

The custom builder gains by getting closer to the efficiency and economy of scale of the production builder. If you build the same house several times, you find that you can build that house more efficiently and cost effectively. The mistakes you make in the first house can be avoided the second time you build it. If you build an entirely new plan every time, you're always at the bottom of the learning curve. If you build the same house several times, but modify it to the needs of the individual buyer, you gain the efficiency you're looking for, without giving up the ability to satisfy each client's particular needs. The custom builder can also increase his volume, since each house requires less hand holding, thereby increasing his profits.

The Future's Not What It Used to Be

What the custom builder excels at is managing customers and guiding them thorough the decision making process. However, by simplifying that process, the custom builder actually increases the comfort level of the buyer, and makes the homebuilding experience more enjoyable.

Production builder advantages

The production builder is also moving toward semi-custom, because that's what buyers want. The days where the builder can tell buyers what they want are over. Today's buyers are more demanding and sophisticated. In addition, production builders realize that higher profits can be made in the high end of the market, which has often been the market niche of the custom builder.

The other reason that production builders are moving in this direction is that new technology makes it easier than before. Three-dimensional CAD (Computer Assisted Design) programs make modifying an existing plan a piece of cake. They can even show the prospective buyer what the home will look like (inside and out) after the change. The builder can pre-price the standard changes so that the house doesn't have to be reestimated. By streamlining the process, buyers get the flexibility they want, and the builders maintain their efficiency.

If you're a custom builder, it's time to start thinking about moving to the semi-custom arena. You should develop a portfolio of plans that you can easily modify to meet individual needs. If you don't, and wait until the production builders start stealing your customers by customizing their houses, you may find that the grass is brown no matter where you sit.

The Future's Not What It Used to Be

The Search for the Magic Bullet

Americans are noted for wanting an instant fix, a magic cure. If we're overweight, we don't want to follow an extensive exercise program or a change our eating habits. We want a pill that dissolves fat effortlessly. Millions of people fall prey to get-rich quick-schemes that promise wealth without effort. In all these situations, we look for the quick fix, the easy solution. Our slogan seems to be, "The problem with instant gratification is that it takes too long."

Unfortunately, life rarely works that way. Every time we try to take a shortcut it seems to get us into more trouble. Anything worth having seems to require an incredible amount of effort. As they say in the exercise business "no pain, no gain." And yet, we continue to go through management fad after management fad, expecting this or that new idea will solve all our management problems. Whether it's Total Quality Management, reengineering, downsizing, or right sizing, we jump in enthusiastically and then are disappointed when those stubborn problems still remain.

Different solutions for different problems

The problem with management fads isn't that they aren't good ideas. Management by objectives, for example, is a great way to structure management goals toward desired results. But it only solves part of the problem. There are still the problems of implementation, team building, and skill training, for example. Let's face it, if solving problems was easy, everyone could do it.

Law of unintended consequences

Another reason no magic bullet exists is the difficulty of anticipating all the things that can go wrong. As the T-shirt says, "Stuff happens." The law of unintended consequences says that whenever you try to solve one problem, you introduce something new into the equation which creates other problems.

For example, suppose you have trouble finding and hiring good people. You need to hire a second superintendent. You look around and see that your competitor has a great superintendent. You offer him a 20% salary increase to work for you. He agrees, but now your first superintendent is unhappy because you went outside and paid someone big bucks to compete with him for your attention. Your competitor then hires *your* superintendent away from you, at a 20% increase in salary, and now you're back where you started, and paying more money besides. That's the law of unintended consequences.

Continuous incremental improvement

While there may not be a magic bullet, that doesn't mean things can't be improved. The way to improve them is not all at once, but in small steps. Improvement is a continual process. No matter how good your product design is today, it can be better. No matter how strong your marketing message, it can be stronger. The better you are, the more you create value in the marketplace and the higher your profit margins can be. With the competition in such a state of flux, the builder who is resting on his laurels is the one who's ensuring his early demise. In fact, the best builders are those who realize that true success is a never ending journey of change and improvement.

Running a building business is basically about solving problems: people problems, money problems, and production problems. Solving problems takes intelligence, lots of hard work, a commitment to change, and a long-term vision. If you're waiting for the magic bullet, you're missing the opportunity to do something about your problems now.

So, What's the Problem?

Sooner or later every business encounters problems. To solve them, we must understand what's causing them. This process of diagnosis and analysis is called troubleshooting, and it's one of the most important skills a builder can have. Why? Because in home building there's no shortage of trouble.

You usually know you have a problem when unwanted symptoms occur. You notice that your profits aren't as high as you were expecting. Or you get an unusual number of customer complaints. Maybe sales are lower than anticipated. Maybe the houses aren't being completed on time, or they have a high number of items on the final checklist. Whatever the symptom, it usually indicates a deeper problem.

Sometimes the symptoms themselves are life-threatening and must be addressed immediately. If you're bleeding, there's nothing wrong with applying a Band-Aid before you find out how you got cut. But once you apply the Band-Aid, don't stop there. First aid is not a permanent fix.

The right diagnosis

To diagnose a problem, you must identify the possible causes and eliminate them one at a time. Suppose you discover that you're losing too many bids based on your estimates. Ask yourself: Are my prices too high? Am I failing to convince potential clients that my services are worth a few extra dollars and represent better value? And, if my prices are too high, why are they too high? Am I paying too much for materials and services? Am I using out-of-date pricing for my estimates? Am I double counting components, or adding in too high a fudge factor for unknowns? Can I move some of the unknowns to allowances to reduce the risk? Is my overhead too high based on my volume? Can I reduce the overhead or increase the volume? As you can see, the basic symptom (losing too many bids) can have a multitude of causes. If you pick the first possible cause that comes to mind, you may not solve the problem. Don't jump the gun by applying a quick fix; make sure it's the right fix.

The Future's Not What It Used to Be

A permanent solution

You want not only to correct the problem, but also to prevent its recurrence. You must outline the steps to be taken, assign responsibility for implementation, and set a deadline for completion. Then make sure the tasks are done. Without follow-through, things fall between the cracks, people revert to old behavior patterns, and you soon find you have to solve the problem again.

Above all, when troubles arise, don't ignore them. Many builders act like Linus in the comic strip "Peanuts" when he said, "There's no problem so big you can't run away from it." Often we don't want to deal with unpleasant realities – we might have to fire someone, or face something about ourselves we don't want to admit. But running away just makes matters worse.

Improving your business is the process of diagnosing and solving problems. So never hesitate to ask, "What's the problem?"

Set Yourself Apart

Competition in the home building industry is getting tougher every day. For your business to survive and grow, you must stand out from the competition. Unless you are somehow different from the other builders, you'll have to go head to head with them on price, which ultimately leads to lower profits.

Here are five ways to set yourself apart from the competition. You should be using several, if not all, of these strategies.

1. Better design

No matter how good your construction quality is, if the house doesn't meet the prospects' physical and lifestyle needs or capture their imagination, they're not going to buy. Good design shouldn't cost more to build than mediocre design. In fact, it should cost less. Good design should be easier to build, in addition to living well and having curb appeal

2. Better location

To make the most of value and consumer demand, choose good quality and premium lots without overpaying. A beautiful house in a bad location is still a bad location. But if you've got the house with the lot on the golf course, and that's what the buyer wants, then you've set yourself apart from the competition. Even at the bottom of the market, avoid low prices that could tempt you into deal-killing negatives such as power lines and noisy roadways.

3. Better value

Notice: I did not say lower price. Value is determined by the benefits divided by the costs. Just as most of your buyers do not drive the lowest priced car, they also don't want the lowest priced house. Look for ideas you can add to your houses that increase the value without greatly increasing the cost. Avoid expensive materials and features that may, or may not, increase value in the prospects' eyes.

4. Better service

You should make buying or building a house with you as easy and pleasant as possible. Streamline your financing and selection procedures. Improve the response time on customer service requests. Return phone calls promptly. If the answer is no, then say no, but say it quickly. And always go the extra mile to make sure realistic expectations are created and met.

5. Better marketing

After you've done all these things to set yourself apart from the competition, make sure you let your prospective buyers know about it. But don't rely on marketing alone to show your distinctiveness.

In setting yourself apart, don't try to be different just for the sake of being different. Remember: A difference, to *be a* difference, must *make* a difference. But if you set yourself apart and provide real benefits to your buyers, you'll survive and thrive when the competition gets tough.

Time for a Change

L et's face it: The world is constantly changing. The market's changing, people's expectations are changing, and, if you don't want to get left behind, you have to change. Builders are often resistant to change, however. They're afraid of new technologies, new ways of doing things.

There is a right way and a wrong way to make changes. The wrong way is to change everything you're doing and do something completely different. This is known as "throwing the baby out with the bath water." The right way is to change incrementally, keeping the things that work while finding new things that work better.

Here are four areas to look at in your company to determine whether or not you need to change.

1. Change the design
People live differently today than they did 20 or 30 years ago. Families are smaller, and if there are two parents in a family, it's likely they both work. Entertaining is less formal, and people are looking for more luxury. Housing needs are more diverse. Examine the spec houses you build to make sure they appeal to today's consumers.

2. Change the product selection
The components can have a major effect on the value consumers perceive a house to have. Look for affordable products with name-brand recognition, and then use that recognition in your marketing efforts. You may even be able to get co-op advertising money by mentioning products in your ads. Also look for low-cost items (such as upgraded moulding) that add perceived value to the entire house at a small price.

3. Change your organization
For the highest productivity, you must have dedicated and motivated employees. To motivate your employees, you may need to change your compensation program. Tie compensation to corporate goals, and don't forget to stress nonmonetary compensation. Letting people know

they're doing a good job is often the best motivation. Also, look at your retirement program. You should have strong programs in place.

4. Change your image

You can make a major improvement in your corporate image without spending much money. Hire a free-lance designer to rework your logo and letterhead. Redo your corporate brochure, and make sure it lists the major benefits of buying from your company. Make sure your signage is attractive and visible. Spruce up your office with a new coat of paint, new artwork, or a new layout. You always want to make a good first impression.

Continual incremental improvement gave the Japanese auto industry its competitive edge. It's time to begin applying it to your building business as well.

Get Creative

One of the traits that separates truly successful builders from their competition is creativity. Whenever successful builders see a problem or an opportunity, they develop creative solutions. Notice that we said creativity, not originality. Creativity is applying a new solution to a problem. It may not be original, but if it works, it's creative. Creativity takes the known and familiar and applies it in new ways. Creativity can be applied to every aspect of the building business – especially product design, management, and marketing.

Product design

One obvious application for creativity is in house designs. Look yours over. Are they tired plans from the 1960s and 1970s? Are your competitors providing more of the features buyers want? Is there a demand in your market for a first-floor master bedroom design? Offer one. Does your competition offer better moulding details or better flow between rooms? You can add similar features to your houses without copying your competitors. (Remember: Direct copying is illegal.) It's ideas you want – the way something works. How you apply the idea is the measure of your creativity.

Management

Originality says that you have to create every form letter and every management procedure from scratch. Creativity says to find the best letters and forms available and then adapt them to your needs. Creativity can also help you use your subs and suppliers in new ways – empowering them to solve minor problems for you on the spot and then let you know what they did. It allows you to treat employees and outside businesses as collaborators who contribute ideas as well as labor.

Marketing

Who says you have to spend big bucks on brochures and media advertising to have effective marketing? The most effective marketing is word of mouth. Use your creativity to "create" word of mouth through an active referral program with past clientele. If you just call one or two every day and ask for a referral, your sales will increase and it will cost you almost nothing.

Creativity could also mean having a designer develop a strong visual identity and using it again and again in all your marketing efforts. Creativity means finding the right message and hammering it home.

What can you do if you don't feel you're creative? Find people who are and work with them. Recognizing other people's creativity is as important as being creative yourself. Remember: it's the results that matter, not the originality. By being creative you can build on the ideas and accomplishments of others, adapt them to your situation, and create higher profits and productivity for yourself.

The Future's Not What It Used to Be

The Need for a Sense of Urgency

Everyone who has studied marketing understands the "call to action," a carefully crafted presentation designed to motivate the reader/listener into acting *right now*. A more interesting analysis, however, revolves around management's ability to create a sense of urgency not in the mind of the buyer, but in the corporate consciousness of the entire organization – staff, subcontractors, and suppliers. For a "do-it-now" attitude has several ramifications far beyond motivating a reluctant buyer. It is, in fact, about our ability to implement and accomplish goals within our organization.

As we work with principals of building companies, I can't help but notice how often they are frustrated by the unwillingness or inability of subordinates to push hard toward the speedy achievement of specific goals and tasks. In the end, management is about what you can accomplish, and a sense of urgency is a powerful tool in getting things done.

Here are four reasons that a corporate sense of urgency is so critical to your success:

Credibility

Consistently delivering goods and services on or ahead of schedule is the foundation of a company in which customers can believe. Some companies take this the extra mile and create corporate legends based around performance. Once it becomes part of your corporate culture, it becomes a powerful incentive to maintain performance.

Opportunity

Many times, outstanding opportunities are lost for lack of prompt action. Opportunities are time sensitive. If you don't seize them, companies that are driven by a sense of urgency will. The difference between Microsoft and Digital Research (remember them?) was that Microsoft had a sense of urgency about delivering an operating system for the new IBM PC. Microsoft became the dominant software system, and Digital Research became a footnote in computer history.

Lost Profits

The difference between acceptable profits and outstanding profitability is the last small increment of volume after the overhead has been paid. A sense of urgency allows the company to reach the profit potential of the last dollar of volume.

Pride

Teams that accomplish a lot, that produce more and better work products than the competition, are proud of who they are what they can do. This "Team Esteem" is critical to creating an organization that thrives on challenge and is capable of overcoming obstacles.

In all this urgency, however, there lurks a danger. There is a difference between a sense of urgency and a sense of crises. There can be a fine line between creating a sense of urgency and creating a sense of burnout. You don't want to drive your best people into leaving you for the competition. You don't want people so driven by getting things done that they sacrifice quality for quantity. You can avoid that trap simply by injecting some fun and humor into the workplace. A company that enjoys a sense of urgency and "Team Esteem" is energized by their accomplishments and pride.

Good attitudes become good work habits. Having fun *and* getting things done is what it's all about.

How to Create a
Sense of Urgency

Now that you know you need your company to operate with a sense of urgency, let's look at how to create one. Motivating employees to "hustle" and be highly productive starts with the right people – people who want to succeed, who understand teamwork, and who are capable of change. We have the responsibility as managers to motivate our associates through reward (praise and financial remuneration) and education (providing the tools and skills to become better). Neither of these will be effective, however, if directed at employees who are intellectually or emotionally incapable of improvement. Once you have people who respond to motivation, here are some ways to create a sense of urgency:

Lead by example

Unless you demonstrate a sense of urgency, no one else will either. The trick is putting on the pressure without turning everything into a crisis and wearing everyone out. Urgency means setting priorities. When everything is a four-alarm fire, people quickly learn to treat real four-alarm fires as if they're routine. If you expect your people to perform, then *you* have to perform. If you're out playing golf every afternoon, don't expect the staff to feel an overwhelming need to finish *now*!

Set specific deadlines

Some people work better under a deadline. It communicates more urgency when you say, "I need this done by 3:00 P.M. on Thursday" than if you say, "Get this done as soon as possible." Remember the corollary to the Peter Principle[1]: "Work expands to fit the time allotted." Giving someone more time to get a job done rarely improves the performance; instead, more time is spent fussing with details. Keep your deadlines short but reasonable.

[1] The Peter Principle: "In a hierarchy, employees tend to rise to the level of their incompetence."

Raise the bar

Sometimes people don't perform to their potential because no one expects them to. By requiring your people to find effective solutions and praising their performance, you set new standards and reward the behavior you're trying to instill. Let them know that *they* are responsible for results, and they'll respond accordingly.

Encourage efficiency

Often the real time-savers and creative solutions come from the staff, not from the top. But unless you encourage new ideas, they'll never surface. Rules aren't made to be broken – they're made to be rewritten. When people see that their solutions are accepted and implemented, you'll be amazed at how creative they'll become.

Make urgency fun

There's a fine line between a dynamic, action-oriented workplace and a stressful, ulcer-producing one. That difference is rooted in anagement's attitude. People *do* miss deadlines, especially when you're asking them to do more and to pick up the pace. Accept human limitations, while at the same time encouraging results.

If your employees are operating from a healthy sense of urgency, and they know they're allowed to make mistakes while getting results, they'll be more productive. And you'll be more profitable.

The Problems of Success

These have been good years for the building industry. Housing starts are up, and the growth in the stock market has meant that more people have had the means to indulge their housing dreams. Along with that success have come reports of the typical problems of success – shortage of subcontractors, and not enough hours in the day.

The problems of success are more enjoyable than the problems of failure. For one thing, you can cry all the way to the bank. For another, you have more resources to devote to solving your problems. However, the problems of success can be aggravating and even fatal if left unattended. Today's small and profitable company can become tomorrow's floundering corporation with unfocused management, bloated overhead, and burned-out employees.

Here are some of the major ways problems of success manifest themselves:

1. Not enough time
2. Lack of management control and focus
3. Difficulty in finding the right people
4. Employee burnout and high turnover
5. Inadequate support systems
6. Inadequate capital

If you're experiencing some of these problems, here are some suggestions on what to do about it.

1. Manage growth

Though you hate to turn down revenue, if you find yourself running out of control, the first thing to do is to put a limit on growth. Be more selective in your clients. Raise your prices. Say *no* to projects that are marginal. Limit yourself to a particular market niche. It's better to be a small successful company than a large unprofitable one.

2. Find the right people

In a tight labor market, this can be difficult. Start by retaining the people you already have. Talk to your subs. Find out if they would be

The Future's Not What It Used to Be

able to shift additional crews to your work in exchange for quicker pay. Retain sub loyalty by paying on time.

3. Improve your support systems

If you're struggling with inadequate management systems now, it will only get worse as you grow. Start with the money management systems. Are you getting the financial reports you need, when you need them, in a format that is quickly understood?

Replace your obsolete equipment. When we moved our offices, we bought several new Pentium II computers. They've already paid for themselves through increased productivity.

4. Secure additional capital

Increased growth leads to increased capital demands. You're buying more land, purchasing more materials, hiring more subcontractors. Managing cash flow becomes ever more critical. Talk to your banker ahead of time and secure extended lines of credit. Find some outside investors to finance spec homes and land deals. And make sure you don't fall victim to creeping overhead.

By managing growth and watching cash flow, you can transform the problems of success into greater profits.

Staying Focused

One thing that sets successful builders apart is that they keep focused. Imagine you're driving the road of life. Direction is knowing where you're trying to go and staying on the right road. Focus is paying attention to your driving so you don't go off the road into the ditch. Both direction and focus are necessary to arrive safely.

Recently I was speaking with a Midwestern builder who had made quite a bit of money doing teardowns and rebuilds in close-in neighborhoods. So what did he do? He built a large, expensive spec house in a far-out subdivision that had many other builders, spent $50,000 decorating it, and watched the house sit for a year. Not only was the spec house a loser, but think about the opportunity cost of the teardowns that didn't happen.

The Diagnosis

It's easy to tell if you have a focus problem. Do you start lots of projects but leave many unfinished? Do you put most of your effort into the parts of the business you enjoy the most rather than the parts that get the most results? If you think you have a focus problem, ask yourself these questions:

Position. Who are we? Who are our customers? What is our market niche?

Balance. Do we pay attention to all the different aspects of the business (marketing, organization, financing, and construction)?

Structure. Are we organized for success? Do we have the right resources, tools, and systems to accomplish the mission?

Results. What efforts have made the most money in the past? Where did we lose money? Are we spending our time on those activities that made money and avoiding those that lost money?

The Cure

The answers to these questions (or the lack of them) will let you know if you have a focus problem. If you are unfocused, what can you do? If you have a problem finishing things, find someone who's a finisher to work with. You start the projects and let them carry them to completion. Or make a rule for yourself: no new projects until you complete the old one.

If you have a tendency to go off in new directions, it may be because you're bored with your business and are looking for a new challenge. You need to find an outlet for that creativity so you aren't tempted to head off into a blind alley. Ask yourself: In what parts of the business can I use my creativity without changing direction? Maybe you need new designs, or new marketing strategies, rather than a new business direction. Or find a creative outlet outside the business.

The grass is always greener on the other side – until you get there. If you're on the right track and making money, stay on track and keep focused on what you're doing. It isn't hocus-pocus, but it will work magic on your bottom line.

Learning from Your Mistakes

Nobody's perfect, (although for some reason most people believe they're a little closer to perfection than the people around them). Unfortunately, few people are willing to admit their mistakes. We spend a great deal of time and energy covering up the little errors we make. And that is probably the biggest mistake of all.

There's nothing wrong with making mistakes. What's wrong is failing to learn from them and making the same mistakes again and again. So here are some simple guidelines for turning blunders into future success.

■ If you're going to make a mistake, make it quickly, so you can recover from it fast. Early mistakes are usually small mistakes, with little money or ego invested. One software company, Netscape, has even incorporated the "art" of making quick mistakes into its corporate philosophy: "Fail quickly to succeed faster."

■ In business, most mistakes are not life-threatening, so don't worry about them. The business-threatening mistakes are the ones that get buried or postponed until they're so huge it's impossible to correct them.

■ Fear of making mistakes is one of the biggest barriers to getting things done. We're afraid of being penalized for our errors, but inaction due to fear of mistakes is the biggest mistake of all. That's why, when faced with a problem, you need to *do* something, even if it's the wrong thing. If it's the wrong thing, you'll know it and be able to discover more quickly what the right thing is.

So, how can you use the fine art of making mistakes to improve your company?

■ Admit your own mistakes. This will create a healthier working environment for learning and growing. It will also amaze your employees, since bosses rarely admit to bad judgment or decisions. Who knows? You may become a living legend.

The Future's Not What It Used to Be

■ Reward your staff for making mistakes, as long as they admit and correct them. The people who make mistakes are the people who are taking risks and trying new things. The people who don't are the ones who are simply doing the same things over and over. If you punish people for taking risks, you don't create an error-free environment, you simply stifle creativity and opportunity.

■ Learn the lessons from your mistakes so you don't repeat them in the future. While it's okay to make errors, making the same error over and over again is inexcusable.

■ One way to avoid the fear of making mistakes is to not call them mistakes. Instead, call mistakes "experiments" (which may fail or succeed and tell you something either way). Or simply adopt the Japanese business strategy of continuous incremental improvement: Rather than eliminate mistakes, look for new ways to continually improve upon your procedures.

Whatever strategy you decide to adopt, you must realize that success is not the absence of failure. Rather, success requires taking risks, making and learning from mistakes, and getting better and more competitive.

Abort, Retry, Fail

Those of you who used personal computers in the bad old days before Windows remember the common error message indicating disk failure: *Abort, Retry, Fail.* Whenever you saw them you said to yourself "Oh dear, what do I do now?"

Abort means stop doing what you're doing, assess the situation to determine what you're doing wrong, and then try again. It gives you breathing room, and allows you to quit wasting time, energy, and effort on something that isn't working, and use that energy instead to figure out what's wrong.

Retry means do whatever you were doing one more time. Maybe it will work this time. If the idea was basically a sound one, this can prove to be a good strategy. Sometimes you have to try something more than once before it works.

Fail means to give up what you were trying to do totally. Maybe it was a bad idea to start with. Maybe it wasn't a bad idea, but the market wasn't ready.

The three strategies above are the basic ways of dealing with plans going wrong. Things go wrong in the building business more often than we care to admit. In fact, if nothing ever goes wrong, you're either not trying anything new or you're blissfully unaware of what's really happening. People who don't make mistakes aren't learning or growing. They're stuck in the old ways of doing things and, in fact, may be making the biggest mistake of all.

Smart builders constantly look for things that went wrong, not so they can point fingers or cast blame, but so they can correct these problems before major damage occurs, and prevent them from happening in the future. The most important thing is to learn from your mistakes. *Why* was it a bad idea? Was it flawed in conception or in execution? Did you fail to secure enthusiastic support for the program from the staff and employees tasked to implement it? Were you inflexible, unwilling to make adjust the program along the way?

Detecting problems early requires an early warning system. Most builders I know have early problem suppression systems. People often get into trouble for making mistakes, and since people don't like getting into trouble, they try to fix the mistakes before you find out about them. They then cover up any evidence that there was ever a mistake. To create an early warning system, you have to take your employees aside and tell them the following:

1. We expect people to make mistakes

In our company, you won't be punished for making mistakes as long as you let me know about them immediately. What does make us unhappy are people who refuse to learn from their mistakes.

2. Mistakes are opportunities to eliminate future problems

By learning from our mistakes, we can find ways to avoid problems in the future. After all, it's *our* problem, if it occurs.

3. In order to remain competitive, we must constantly improve our company

Wherever we can, we should be on the lookout for *potential* problems in products, procedures, and dealing with customers. What problems can we eliminate *before* they happen?

Whatever the cause, whenever you're faced with a difficult situation remember these three little words: *Abort, Retry, Fail*. They'll help you pick the right strategy to overcome the problem and be more competitive in the future.

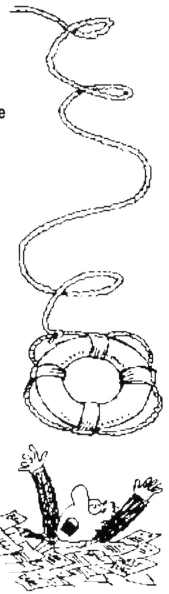

Get Ready for the Future

I am constantly amazed by the number of builders and contractors who consistently ignore the incredible changes that have occurred in the industry as a result of the computer revolution. A few months ago, I met a builder who told me he didn't need a computer because his accountant had one! Somewhere, in the back of his mind, he had the idea that computers were used primarily for accounting. "What about your word processing?" I asked him. "What about your estimates? Does your accountant do those, too?"

The changes in the past 10 years are only the tip of the iceberg. Personal computers are not only inexpensive, but they have become powerful tools for financial management, marketing, scheduling, estimating, and residential design. The small builder and contractor who learns to use these tools to his advantage will grow and prosper. Those who bury their heads in the sand and continue to do things the old, inefficient way, will ultimately find themselves out of business. As Stewart Brand says in *The Media Lab*[1], "When a new technology rolls over you, you're either part of the steamroller, or you're part of the road."

Take residential design, for example. If you're a remodelor or a design/build firm, the computer offers visualization tools that are simply not available any other way. Using one of the new 3-D CAD programs, you can quickly create a home design and then walk around inside it. Your clients can also walk around inside it, examining the spaces from any angle. They can actually see what the finished house will look and feel like inside. This eliminates the "I didn't know it was going to look like that!" reaction that is the bane of a custom builder's life. By visualizing the completed design in 3-D early in the process, you can avoid costly mistakes and changes. Moving a wall in a CAD program costs you a few minutes of time. Moving a wall in a nearly finished house can cost thousands of dollars.

[1] Stewart Brand, *The Media Lab: Inventing the Future at MIT.* Penguin Books,1988.

The Future's Not What It Used to Be

Suppose model homes are the way you show your product to potential clients. By using computer technology, you can increase the number of homes you can show your clients, without building new models. How's that for saving money?

Now suppose your competition has a 3-D model home to show his clients, and all you have is a blueprint. Who looks like the industry leader? Who is going to close more sales? Who is going to make the buyer more comfortable? Who is going to eliminate costly mistakes that might be avoided with a "tour" of the unbuilt house'? Who is going to be in business five years from now'?

Once upon a time, all that computing power was beyond the reach of the small builder. Now, a Pentium multimedia computer that can provide all this power is available for under $2,000. If you're not really ready to learn a CAD program, you can buy pre-designed 3-D model homes that will run on your computer. Or, you can hire a company that will convert your existing plan into a 3-D CAD model.

I'm sorry, but you've run out of excuses. The future is coming. Are you going to be ready?

The Future's Not What It Used to Be

Appropriate Technology

The personal computer revolution has had a major impact on the way everyone does business today, and that includes the building industry. Builders now use computers for accounting, scheduling, word processing and design.

But, like all new technologies, there is a downside. Computers can improve productivity, allow us to do things we've never done before, and provide better management information. They can also cause major headaches and suck up time like a black hole as we try to learn new programs and integrate new systems throughout the company.

So, what is the appropriate use of technology? When it leads to productivity increases. Today computers are easier to use and easier to learn. Paradoxically, as the technology becomes more complex, the user interaction becomes more transparent. However, despite the new user friendliness, computers are not for everyone. Not everyone has good typing skills, or enjoys opening and closing files, or sending information in and out, or dealing with software glitches. When the computer works as expected, it's wonderful. When it doesn't, it's a pain.

A good example of an appropriate use of technology is builder-management computer software. These are large, complex programs that integrate accounting, scheduling, purchase orders, and marketing management. By combining all these functions into one place, they increase efficiency by avoiding duplication of effort and by better managing the entire process of building a home.

This is, on the face of it, a good thing. But to get the full benefit of program integration, some of these applications try to computerize field operations as well. This may mean buying laptop computers for superintendents, and training field personnel to use the new program. Laptops are expensive, fragile pieces of equipment, not suited to the rough-and-tumble world of onsite construction. But the biggest cost is the time and effort in learning to use them. Superintendents are good at building houses and getting things done. They aren't necessarily good at the skills needed for computer operations. Some superintendents, of course, will love the idea of having computers on the job site. Others will hate them and feel they're a distraction.

Until people become proficient in the new technology, productivity will fall, rather than increase. Many builders have invested thousands of dollars in software, plus uncounted hours trying to master the program, only to give up in frustration and put the software back.

Wouldn't it be nice if computers adapted to the way we do things, rather than having to adapt our behavior to the way they do things? Now if we could just get the computer to fill out the forms and pound the nails, life would be great.

2
Putting the Custom in Customer

Levi Strauss, the famous manufacturer of blue jeans, now has stores where your measurements are taken. A few weeks later, a pair of jeans are delivered to your door, custom tailored to your exact dimensions. What does it cost? About 20% more than a pair of "off-the-shelf" jeans.

At Neiman Marcus, they keep records of the purchasing patterns of their frequent customers, and call you when something arrives that they think you might like.

This kind of attention to the needs and wants of the customer is becoming increasingly important for all kinds of businesses. The mass market is being segmented into smaller individual markets. In the home building industry, concentrating on individual wants and needs is the name of the game. Everyone is different, and unless you can satisfy those individual needs and wants, you're out of the game.

Before you can satisfy those needs, you first need to understand what they are. You need good listening, coupled with strong communication and negotiation skills. The customer may not always be right, but if you aren't paying attention to them, you'll always be wrong. Welcome to the age of mass customization.

"I cannot give you the formula for success, but I can give you the formula for failure: Try to please everybody."

— Henry B. Swope

It's All About Them

Have you ever been to a party, and the person next to you talked on and on about himself, and his job, and his family. In the meantime, you couldn't get a word in edgewise about *you* and *your* family and *your* career. Did you think, "Boy, what a fascinating person"? I don't think so. We have a word for that kind of person: a bore. And boring is one thing you don't want your marketing to be.

One of the biggest mistakes builders make in marketing is that they feel they have to explain to the buyer who they are. They begin by telling the buyer how long they've been in business, and how they build a quality home. But it's not about you. It's about *their* needs, *their* wants, and *their* egos.

Keep your ego out of it

It's hard for builders to keep their egos out of their work. After all, they pour their heart and soul into it, and it often represents their creative, as well as their management skills. But just as in conversation, the trick is to engage your customers' egos, and keep your ego out of it. Don't tell them what a wonderful builder you are... tell them that they deserve the best builder, and they'll infer the rest. Don't tell them how your bedrooms are luxurious, tell them that they've worked hard to enjoy that luxury. You're saying the same thing, but from a different viewpoint – theirs.

It's about their needs and wants

Needs are the minimum threshold criteria that will satisfy a buyer. If they say they need three bedrooms, then they won't consider a house with two bedrooms, but might consider one with four. A two-car garage may satisfy their needs, but a three-car garage satisfies their wants. The more wants you satisfy, the better chance you have to sell the home.

Perception is reality

Buyer's perceptions are everything in marketing effectiveness. If doesn't matter if you're the best builder in the world, with the lowest prices, if buyers are unaware of that fact, and don't perceive the quality or the value. To create a perception, you have to start with their psychological state, their perceived needs and wants, and then work with those perceptions to create your message.

To communicate benefits, you have to look at your product from the viewpoint of the customer. How does this make their life better? What's in it for *them*? A feature is simply an aspect of the product. A benefit is what this feature does for them. Most builders make the mistake of telling the buyer all about the features of the home (the size, the number of bedrooms, etc.) and forget to sell the benefits.

The art of embedded questions

One way to engage a prospect's ego, without being blatant about it, is through the use of an embedded question. An embedded question is simply a statement that is rephrased as a question. By asking it as a question, you engage their participation, and secure their agreement. If you state "You'd *love* to live in a Pinnacle Home," the reader may respond, "Says who?" If you ask, "Wouldn't you love to live in a Pinnacle Home?" their answer is "I might … let me find out more."

The most important thing you can do in improving your marketing message is to rewrite it from the viewpoint of the buyer's needs and wants and emotions. Put them in the center. Engage their egos. Get your ego out of it. After all, it's about them, not you.

Putting the Custom in Customer

Crossing the Comfort Threshold

Whenever we make a decision to buy something, it creates a certain anxiety within us. "Am I making the right decision? Am I paying the right price? Does this product meet my needs and wants? What happens if I make the wrong decision?" We look for information that will satisfy our expectations and reduce our anxiety. Until we feel comfortable in that decision, we will not go ahead with it. Before we act, we must cross the "comfort threshold."

This is true in homebuilding, and even more so in custom home building. That's because a home is intimately linked with a family's perception of comfort and because much of what the consumer buys is intangible. How does the buyer know that the house is built correctly? How does he or she know the house won't have major maintenance headaches later on? Will the builder stand behind the warranty if there are problems? Issues such as builder integrity and fears of price over-runs and project delays can cause buyers to hesitate in their decision to purchase. Adding to the consumer's unease is the fact that buying a house is such a major investment, one the buyer will have to live with for years to come. In the end it comes down to "Do I like and trust this builder enough to give him a significant amount of money?" Here are five things you can do to help you cross that comfort threshold:

1. Confront the anxiety

Simply by acknowledging that buying a home can be stress-inducing creates an atmosphere of honesty and rapport with the client. "Finally," the buyer says, "a builder who understands what I'm feeling."

2. Use past experience as an indicator of reliability

Builders often tell buyers how long they've been in business. What they fail to say is why that's important to the buyer. It's important because it means you've been successful in the past in meeting buyer needs and that you'll likely be around for many years to come. It also means that you'll make fewer mistakes, since you made your mistakes a long time ago.

36   **Putting the Custom in Customer**

3. Use testimonials as third-party endorsements

Testimonials, to be effective, must address the heart of the buyer's concerns. You should use testimonials that talk about the experience of building with you, as well as quality of work and family comfort concerns.

4. Use information to relieve anxiety

The more people know about the benefits they will receive and what to expect in the process, the less anxiety they have. We call this process, "creating realistic expectations." This means having good specifications and buyer information guides. You don't have to promise them the moon. In fact, the more detailed and realistic the information is, the more credibility you will have.

5. Simplify the process

Reduce the number of decision points and clearly spell out the step-by-step process they will go through before they move into their new home. If you do this graphically, it will have a much stronger impact. They can see: "Oh, that's not so bad. They really know what they're doing."

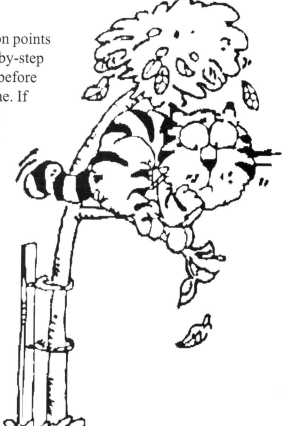

Once you understand that selling a home is really a process of getting the buyer to trust you as a builder, and what you can do to increase that trust, you're on your way to crossing the comfort threshold.

The Power of Choice

Providing people with choices is a powerful marketing concept. People like to feel that they have options. It gives them a sense of control over their destiny, and it focuses their attention on making a decision. "Do you prefer product A or product B" is a better sales approach than "What do you think? You want to buy, or what?"

Remember, buyers *always* have a choice. They can choose to buy, or not buy. They can buy from you, or from someone else. To get them to buy, and buy from you, you have to give them the choices they want, in a way that they like.

Too few choices

Henry Ford once had over 50% of the world market in automobiles. His philosophy on choices was simple: "You can have any color you want, as long as it's black." That worked fine until General Motors came along and let buyers have their pick of models and colors. Ford lost its market leadership and never quite recovered.

When you give buyers too few choices, they go looking elsewhere to find what they want. This is the way production builders used to think, building the same house over and over again, with no variation. Now you see ads from production builders telling buyers "We do it your way." They've learned that when they don't give buyers the choices they need and want, they lose the sale.

Too many choices

Today, consumers have more choices than ever before. A typical super-market may carry 350,000 different products, including (in one store) 240 brands of pain relievers. Maybe we buy so many pain relievers because we get a headache from making so many choices.

When you give buyers too many choices, they become confused and don't buy *anything*. Making a sale is often a process of reducing uncertainty. This is often the case with the custom builder who gives their clients unlimited choices and provides little guidance. The buyer is often overwhelmed by the decision-making process and decides to buy a production home or an existing home.

Managing choices

The correct solution is to try to give the buyer the right number of choices, organized in a way that makes it easy. The key is to break the decisions into "bite-sized pieces," and simplify the decision-making process. Three ways to do this are preselecting, bundling, and customization.

Preselecting consists of determining the most cost-effective choice for the buyer, and providing this as the default choice. This could mean choosing Andersen Windows, Kohler fixtures, and Corian countertops, and explaining to the buyer why you chose those selections (quality, warranty, brand-name awareness, etc.) If they like those selections, many of their decisions are already made.

Bundling is the process of grouping options into a predetermined package. For example, an upgraded lighting package could include a predetermined number of additional downlights, plus a lighting cove in the dining room. Now, instead of making five or six choices, buyers only have to make one. In addition, they know that the options are designed to work together.

Customization (as opposed to pure custom) presents buyers with a home plan and allows them to make incremental changes in room size and usage. Instead of starting from a blank sheet of paper, their choices are manageable. Options are often pre-packaged and prepriced so they can select from their limited menu.

Both custom builders and production builders need to help their buyers make the right decisions, including the all-important one of who builds their home. Managing the number of choices is a good place to start.

The Power of Pricing

Nothing is more critical to success in a free market society than the prices we choose to place upon our products. Competition, resource management, cash flow, and a myriad of other factors may all intrude into our decision-making process. Yet, in the end, each builder must decide how to price what he or she builds. Prices, in effect, become a shorthand for the value we perceive in a product. If we price too low we leave money on the table and may actually lower the perceived value of the product. If we price too high, we may find ourselves undercut by a more value-conscious competitor. To maximize this power of pricing, here are five key thoughts to remember.

1. Use market-based pricing, not cost-based pricing

Market based is pricing according to the perceived value of the product. Cost-based pricing is based on what it cost you to build. But the reality is that the public doesn't really care what the product costs to build ...they care about what the product will do for them. A software program that costs only a few dollars to produce can be worth hundreds or thousands of dollars, based on its utility. If you use better design and efficient production to increase your product quality, people are willing to pay more, despite your lower cost.

2. Use pricing to create velocity

Not all products are created equal. A good example of this is setting lot premiums. To maximize velocity, you should always increase the price of your best lots and reduce the price of your worst lots. Since the premiums offset the reductions, you still make the same total revenue. This has a tendency to increase velocity on all lots, since the highest-priced lots are perceived as a higher value, and the lowest-priced lots are perceived as a bargain.

3. Use pricing to help people find value

You can use pricing to help people justify their wants. For example, you can show that increasing the size of a home by a few feet can actually lower the price per square foot. Even though the total cost has increased, they feel they get more for their money.

4. Using pricing to influence buyer decisions

Price can be a powerful motivating factor. If people perceive that the price could go up in the near future, or they feel that they are getting a bargain on some add-on items, it can move them from the "interested" to the "yes" category quickly. The danger here, of course, is that lowering the price or selling primarily on the basis of price can lower profits and lower the perceived value.

5. Use pricing to create a product mix

General Motors dominated the auto industry by the simple concept of using pricing to differentiate between buyer segments, and satisfy a wider range of wants and needs. Within a given community, the range of your product can vary by 30%, and you can offer different sized homes tailored to different needs, at different price levels.

Everyone tells you to control costs, increase efficiency, or reduce overhead to increase profit. While all of these are important factors, none of these have the impact on profits that prices do. Don't leave that added revenue on the table simply because you didn't understand the true role of price.

Deal Breakers, Deal Makers

Needs and wants are easily confused.
Listen for the difference.

There are three criteria people use to select what they buy: They buy what they *need*, they buy what they *want*, and they buy it for the best *price*. However, buyers often lie (even to themselves) and tell you that the price is the most important aspect. But no matter how good the price is, if buyers don't need it or want it, they won't buy.

Needs and wants are easily confused. You need food, but you want filet mignon. You need shelter from the elements, but you want an elegant home with a three-car garage. Very few of your buyers actually *need* a home. Most of them already have a place to live. What they think they need is a bigger home, a nicer neighborhood, more storage space, etc. Sometimes the only difference appears to be desire. If you want something badly enough, it becomes a perceived need.

Perceived needs are critical in the process of selling a home. A perceived need is the minimal acceptable criteria for selecting a home. If a home doesn't have those things, it's out of the running. That's what we call a deal breaker. If the buyers perceive that they need a three-car garage, then a two-car garage home is not a contender, no matter how nice it is.

Wants go beyond the minimal acceptable level. The customers may feel they need a Jacuzzi in the bathroom, but a Jacuzzi plus a super shower is what they really want. A lack of perceived needs is a deal breaker. The presence of perceived wants is a deal maker. As a builder, your success depends on how well you cater to those perceived needs and wants. How do you find out what your buyers' perceived needs and wants really are? First, by listening to them. If you read between the lines of what they say, they'll tell you what they need and want. The basic rule of thumb: If they're willing to pay for it, they want it.

You must also look at the marketplace. What are the trends? What's selling in your price range? For example, in some price ranges a three-car garage has moved from being a perceived want to a perceived need. We've become more affluent, with more cars and more toys such as boats and snowmobiles. We need more storage space for all our "stuff."

Sometimes wants and needs are determined by what the buyers have. If they're moving up to a nicer home, and their present home has a entryway that opens immediately on the stairway, that's not what they want in their new home. They already have that. They want something different–and better. They want a hidden stairway, or a grand entrance with curving stairs.

Sometimes a group of little needs and wants can add up to a big need. Better lighting, more distinctive hardware, more prominent moldings and trim – all this can add up to a qualitative difference in their buying decision.

The successful builder is the one who can find, understand, capture and fulfill these perceived needs and wants of the marketplace. Make sure you satisfy those needs and wants before you start worrying about the price.

Putting the Custom in Customer

The Problem with Quality

If everyone claims quality, how do you set yourself apart?

In determining their marketing strategy, the number-one question builders have to answer is "Why should someone buy a home from you, rather than from your competition." I often ask builders that question in seminars, and the number one answer is "Quality." So then I ask all the builders "How many of you here do *not* build a quality house?" No one raises a hand.

That's the problem with quality. If everyone claims it, then using it as the cornerstone of your marketing message doesn't set you apart from the competition. It just becomes another unproven claim, another "Says Who?" contributing to the marketing clutter.

Quality is a threshold issue

The thing you have to understand about quality is that it's a threshold issue. Everyone has a certain level of expectation where quality is concerned. For the buyer to even consider you as their builder, you have to cross that quality threshold. Crossing it doesn't make the sale, it merely means that you're in the game. Now you get to compete with everyone else who crossed that threshold.

The other thing about the quality threshold is that once you cross it, that's it. You can't keep selling more and more quality, because they already have all the quality that they're willing to pay for.

You intuitively understand this when shopping for a car. If you're looking for Lexus quality, then Toyota quality won't do. If you're looking for Toyota quality, you aren't willing to pay for Lexus quality.

Sell the quality benefits

In order to sell quality, you have to translate quality into benefits–things that really make a difference. Why is quality important? Because it means greater comfort. It means your home will last and last. It means higher resale value. It means lower maintenance and lower operating costs. It means greater pride of ownership. Those are the benefits of quality, and benefits are all your buyers understand and care about.

Sell the specifics

Another reason you can't sell quality is that people don't know what it means. They have no basis for comparing it to your competitor's "quality." So if you really want to sell quality, first you have to define it, in specific concrete terms. Once you point out to them what quality means, they can get excited about it. For example, if your definition of quality means 8-inch crown moldings in public areas… then say so. If your competitor only uses 6-inch moldings, you've created a quality difference. If your quality means 6 inches of insulation for greater comfort and energy efficiency, then say so.

Find your competitive advantage and make *that* your definition of quality. If it puts your competitor below the quality threshold, so much the better.

"I never argue with people who charge less than I do. They know what they're worth."

Is Anyone Listening?

**To be a smart builder, you must use an age-old art:
Ask questions and listen to the answers.**

Many builders ask me how to do market research to improve
their companies. I always tell them the same thing: Forget
about statistical market research, surveys, and question-
naires. These methods often simplify the data to the point where it isn't
useful. If you really want to know what to do, just ask.

Ask your customers, ask your employees, and ask the people in
your community. And then do something that is hard for most builders
to do – be quiet and listen.

Listen actively

We often think listening is a passive activity. It isn't. It's hard work
requiring attention, concentration, and an ability to read between the
lines to understand what the speaker is really trying to tell you. Often,
people think you don't really want to hear what they have to say. It's
only when you ask probing questions, seeking clarification and
additional information, that they open up.

There is an art to listening effectively. Follow these simple guidelines to become an effective listener and open the two-way communication channels you need to succeed:

■ Suspend all judgment. You're not there to rebut or argue with the
 perceptions of the person you're listening to. You're there to gather
information and insight.
■ Reassure people that you care about what they have to say. Just
listening without rebutting indicates your interest, but it never hurts to
reinforce your interest by telling people that you want to hear what
they have to say.
■ Probe deeper. Ask people why they feel the way they do. If you
don't understand points they make, ask for clarification. It's amazing
how often we thought we understood what others were saying only to
find out they meant something else entirely.

■ Integrate what employees say into your plans and operations. If your employees see that their ideas have an impact, they'll be encouraged to maintain future communication.

Give a little – get a little

The incredible thing about effective listening is that it also encourages people to listen to you. If you listen to your employees, you will find that they are also much more receptive to your ideas. In addition, it gives them a chance to "own" the solution. If they feel that their ideas contributed to the solution, they will more readily implement new procedures and strategies.

Listening to people shows you care about them — that you value them. As a result you can create a much more unified and smoothly functioning organization. And all you have to do is listen.

The Good, the Bad, and the Ugly

Some clients come into your office and you know they are going to be bad news from the beginning. They bring along their child who can't stop crying, the wife and the husband bicker, and the husband has a list (five pages long) of all the things that went wrong with the last house they built. Face it. All clients are not created equal. There are really three kinds of clients: the good, the bad, and the ugly.

Good clients are a joy to work for. They make decisions on time, they have realistic expectations, and they appreciate your work. Bad clients are really nonclients. They may be easy to work with, but they either don't have (or don't wish to spend) the money it takes to do the job. As a result, they waste your time pursuing them, when you could be making money on good clients.

Ugly clients are a royal pain in the posterior. They constantly change their minds, nitpick over the slightest details, and then withhold final payment as they try to negotiate your fees downward. You end up losing money (as well as tearing your hair out). How can you tell the good from the bad and the ugly before they sign the contract? It's something you learned in kindergarten: stop, look, and listen.

STOP

Don't be so anxious to sign the contract that you don't notice what you're getting into. Building or remodeling a home is like a marriage: If you're going to be working closely with clients, you had better like each other and share mutual goals. Take the time to get to know them and their needs and wants.

LOOK

Be aware of inconsistencies in what they say and want. Look at the way they interact with each other. Make certain that their personality is one you can live with. Look for (and help create) realistic expectations on cost, quality, and schedule.

Putting the Custom in Customer

LISTEN

True listening means asking the right questions and listening "between the lines" for the answers. Ask about their budget, about the value of their existing home, and when they need the work done. Ask psychological questions: Have you built a house before? What was the experience like? What don't you like about your present home? Who will make final selection decisions?

Listen also to your intuition. Can they afford your work, and are they willing to pay for it'? Will they be a pain in the neck to deal with? If they might be difficult but not impossible to deal with, add a little to the price for the aggravation factor. And, if they're a truly ugly client, send them to a competitor.

We once had a potential client who asked us to build a house. He had long lists of things that he wanted to be sure were included in the contract. He haggled over every nickel and dime in the estimate. My partner and I knew this guy was bad news so we tried to discourage him. We told him that some of the items in the estimate might cost more than anticipated, especially in light of his high levels of quality expectations. He was willing to negotiate. We told him that we wouldn't be able to start his house for at least six months. No problem, he said. He'd wait. Finally, we told him that we simply didn't think we could give him the level of service he would require. We suggested he contact our nearest competitor who builds very nice homes and might be able to accommodate him better. So he went there and nearly drove our competitor out of business.

If you stop, look, and listen, you'll often spot the bad and ugly clients early and save the time, energy, and money you might have wasted on them.

Lifecycle Segmentation

Part of your corporate identity and brand image is shaped by the market niches you serve. By finding a small but profitable niche, you can specialize and improve your marketing and customer expertise. There are three basic areas to concentrate on: geographic, demographic, and lifestyle. Geographic segmentation is selecting a town or region (or even a single neighborhood) for your homes. This allows you to minimize your marketing and transportation costs and have a better understanding of your market.

Demographics (age, income, and education) allow you to better understand and serve the needs of a particular segment. If you choose to build upper-level houses, you need to market to upper-income people and not waste your marketing on people who can't afford your work. Concentrating on lifestyle allows you to meet the needs of a segment as it ages and its housing needs change. Many builders were very successful at following the baby boom as it went from start-up housing to move-up, to second move-up, to empty nester.

The lifecycle stages

The lifecycle chart shows the various stages individuals go through as they age, marry, have children, send the children off to school, become empty nesters, and, finally, find themselves single again at the end of their life. Each time a person goes through one of those stages, his or her housing needs change. The segments are: young singles, young couples, young families, mature families, shrinking families, empty nesters, aging couples and aging singles.

Each of these cycles has a particular housing need. Young singles usually live in apartments and rental units. Young couples may live in apartments or starter homes. Young families live in small homes or townhouses. As they age and move up in income, they become candidates for first and second move-up homes. As the children start leaving home their housing needs shrink, even as their need for luxury and status increases. When the children are gone, they may want to move to an empty nester home, with less maintenance and upkeep, but with the same luxury they've become used to. As they become older and less

Putting the Custom in Customer

able to care for the maintenance themselves, they may move back into a condo or apartment, and after a spouse dies, they may choose assisted living arrangements, or move back in with family. Each of these lifecycle segments is further segmented by income, with different housing needs at different income levels.

Finding your niche

To find your niche, use all three segmentation strategies. Choose your location based on the way the neighborhood is moving and on housing trends. Then choose your demographic niche. Do you want to build for middle- or upper-income people? There are more middle-income people out there, but your profit margins may be smaller.

Once you select those two segments, choose the lifestyle segment you want to concentrate on. Then make sure your marketing materials are suited for that market. Does your message address their particular needs and wants? Do you know what their "hot" buttons are, and what sells them on housing? Does your product line reflect those particular buttons? For example, two-income professional couples often want a home office, or even two home offices. Can your homes accommodate that need, and do you tell your buyers how your product is designed to meet their needs?

Building the right product in the right place and getting the right message to the right people is what niche marketing is all about.

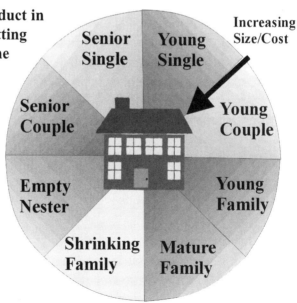

Inform Your Clients

Once you have made a sale and signed a contract for a custom home, you must guide your customers through the complicated process of building the house. One of the most important tools for managing that process is the client information package. A good package can help:

Create realistic expectations

Clients' expectations are often the most difficult part of the building business. Clients with unrealistic expectations about quality or delivery can make your life hell. A good information package helps create realistic expectations before the unrealistic ones become a problem.

Overcome clients' fear of the unknown

Custom-home clients often don't know what to expect, and that fear of the unknown leads to anxiety. You then have to spend a lot of time holding their hands and calming that anxiety. A good information package spells out every step of the process, including the clients' role in it.

Avoid surprises

People don't like surprises (unless of course, they discover something costs less than they expected). But if you let them know ahead of time what to expect, then it's not a surprise.

Protect you legally

In some cases, the courts are deciding that builders have an obligation to inform clients about their rights and responsibilities. By having your clients read and sign a copy of the client information package, you demonstrate "informed consent," as a part of that legal obligation.

Creating the package

If you don't have a client information package, create one. If you do have one, look at it to make sure it's serving your needs, and then make it better. Ask other builders to share copies of their packages with you.

At the very least, the client information package should contain:
- A money section with information about the initial deposit, draw schedule, inspections, and change orders;
- A schedule section that lays out start and finish dates, milestones, and policies on site visits;
- A selections sections that addresses allowances, selections schedule, consequences of delayed selections, and a list of preferred vendors, and;
- A closing section that covers final draw, inspection, walk-through, and service procedures.

Give clients the package at the initial meeting. A good package demonstrates your professionalism and organization and helps you close the sale. It's well worth the effort it takes to create one.

Creating Realistic Expectations

Every builder has had to deal with the problem of the customer who expects too much. The problem with perfection, they seem to feel, is that it's just not good enough. No matter how hard you tried, no matter how much extra work you put into building their home, they were never satisfied.

Creating customer satisfaction is a matter of perception. If clients expect perfection, they will be disappointed no matter how good your quality control is. If they expect no glitches, no delays, no subcontractor mistakes and no cost overruns, then they're living in a dream world, and it's the builder's job to wake them gently.

Building a house is not brain surgery. However, a house is a highly complex, hand-crafted product, involving many different trades and skill levels. We use natural materials such as marble, which are filled with imperfections, some of which make it beautiful. The builder must convey this complexity to his customers at the same time he is trying to convince them of the quality of his work. It can be tricky at times. For the builder, house construction may not be an emotional undertaking. But for the buyer, the process is laden with emotion. When things go wrong in one area, they'll expect problems in other areas as well.

During the negotiation process I have a conversation with the client that goes something like this: "Mr. and Mrs. Jones, do you expect a perfect house?" They look a little startled and say, "What do you mean?" "I mean," I tell them, "that there's no such thing as a perfect house. I'm a very good builder, one of the best, and I've never yet built a perfect house. So if you want a perfect house, tell me now, because it's going to cost you a lot more money." At this point, they say, "Oh, no, we're not looking for perfection. We just want a quality house."

Inevitably, during the final phases of construction, after going over a wall three times to ensure that it is perfectly smooth, I will say, "Mr. and Mrs. Jones, do you remember our conversation about the perfect house?" They will nod, and I say, "We are now approaching that line of searching for the perfect house." They laugh – and are satisfied with the high level of quality we provide.

Let them know at the beginning that things happen on the construction site that are beyond your control. Natural materials will vary. Concrete will crack. People get sick, subcontractors may have to work on other houses, the weather will turn bad and, sooner or later, you'll be behind schedule. If they know such things are inevitable during construction, they can take it in stride.

If buyers expect perfection, they will always be disappointed. But if you have created realistic expectations from they beginning, they will be thrilled to find that the glass isn't half-empty – it's practically full.

Negotiating with Home Buyers

Negotiation is one of the most important tools in the builder's toolbox. It is a vital step in creating customers and it is often the final step in closing the deal. Here are 10 rules to sharpen your negotiating skills.

1. Never be afraid to ask. You'll never get more than you ask for, only less. If you ask, you might get what you want. The worst they can say is no.

2. Know what you want. Set your goals. Why are you negotiating? What are your goals? What price are you looking for? What price are you willing to accept? What terms and safety/escape provisions do you need? What are you willing to give up to reach your goals? What do you give up first? And, if you can't reach an agreement, then what?

3. Be prepared. Know yourself: your strengths, your weaknesses, your priorities, your goals. Remember, knowledge is power. Be prepared physically, emotionally and intellectually. Believe in yourself, your abilities and your positions.

4. Keep your emotions out of the negotiations. Negotiation is not about being popular. Don't let your need to be liked interfere with your ability to negotiate a good deal. It isn't about you – it's about achieving your goals.

5. Focus on your priorities. Negotiation isn't about "winning." It is about getting what you want. Know when to stop negotiating and start closing. If you can get what you want without negotiating, take it. Remember to keep the big picture and focus on your priorities.

6. Negotiation is about power. You often have more power than you real;ize. Examine the things that give you power – good cash flow, backlog of work, multiple offers – and use them in your negotiation.

Minimize your opponent's strengths by acting as if they weren't important to you.

7. Be willing to take a risk. If you're not willing to walk away from the table, you're not really negotiating. You're just haggling. Like everything in life, risk and reward are directly related.

8. Negotiate in bite size pieces. Resolve the easy problems first. This creates momentum which encourages future agreements, and establishes an investment of time for the other party. He may not be willing to walk away from the negotiation and lose the time he's invested.

9. Never be the first to split the difference. In almost any negotiation, the person to go first is at a disadvantage. The other side can then offer to split the remaining difference and you end up somewhere less than halfway. If you feel you have to go first, here's how to go about it. You say "If I were to offer to split the difference, would you meet me there?" If he accepts, this precludes them from splitting again. If he doesn't accept, ask, "Where would you meet me?" You've now gotten him to split the difference, although not halfway.

10. Support your position. Props and evidence can be powerful factors in supporting and defending your position. Give him a reason to believe you. Typical props: engineering reports, comparative sales figures, appraisals, research reports, letters of credit, letter of authorization, calculation sheets, offers or inquiries from other buyers or sellers.

By learning and applying negotiation skills, you'll increase your financial success. You can also use those skills to increase customer satisfaction and employee productivity. As the saying goes, "You don't get what you deserve in life. You get what you negotiate."

Putting the Custom in Customer

Overcoming Objections

O vercoming objections is a four-step process. Each step is critical in reaching your goal of closing the sale.

Step 1. Acknowledge the objection

Validate the objection. Tell them, "I understand how you feel," or "That's a very good question." *Never* tell them, "What do you mean the price is too high? Don't you know what houses are going for these days?" *Never* say, "You're wrong, that's not a valid objection."

Step 2. Ask for clarification

Make sure you understand the objection. Objections are sometimes tricky. They can be emotional objections masquerading as logical objections, or vice-versa. Ask reflective questions. If they object that the price is too high, reflect back the objection. "The price is too high?" Then keep quiet and let them explain. The buyer could be suffering sticker shock (they don't realize how expensive things are these days). It could be a *relative* price issue, compared to some other product. It could be a cash flow issue (monthly payment). It's important to understand exactly what the objection is. Don't assume you understand.

Step 3. Agree on action if resolved

What you want is a conditional agreement that resolution of the objection will lead to action on the part of the buyer. Ask, "*If* we can resolve this problem, would you buy the home?" If they answer, "We'd seriously consider it," then the negotiation is serious. Then ask, "What other issues are there to resolve?" Only after you identify and overcome all objections are you ready to close the sale.

Step 4. Attain resolution

Finally, you get to overcome the objection.
Seller: "How can we fix this problem?" (Did you have a solution in mind?) Sometimes the best way to overcome an objection is to ask the buyers to overcome it for you. Their solution may be quicker and less expensive than the one you had in mind.

Putting the Custom in Customer

The simplest way to reach an agreement, of course, is to **concede**. "Yes, you're right. We'll take care of that right away." This is a good strategy if the objection won't cost much to overcome. The second simplest is to **compromise**. "That's a good idea. It would normally cost $1,500 to change that, but if this will satisfy your objections, we could do it for you for $1,200." The third way, **convince**, is the most difficult. There are three major ways to do this: **A**djust their perception, **A**ccentuate benefits, and **A**dvance **A**lternatives.

Adjust their perception by reframing the objection. Put the objection in context. For example, if price is the objection, reframe the cost in terms of the total value of the home. "Yes, this house is a little more expensive than the other one. But the difference is less than 3% of the total cost. Look how much more you get for that small increase." Or, reframe in terms of monthly payments. "This house costs $5,000 more. That means that your payments are only an additional $45 per month."

Accentuate the benefits. Stress your expertise, professionalism, experience, and quality control. Show how you really save them money in the long run. "Yes, our homes may cost a little more than our competition's. But, when you compare the value, quality, and service, they are more than worth the small difference in price."

Advance Alternatives. These are the "what if" scenarios designed to eliminate the cause of the objection. For example, if a room in a model is too dark, ask, "What if we added a window in the house we build for you? What if we added additional built-in lighting? Would it be worth an additional $500 for you to add a window to resolve this problem?"

Objections are wonderful things because they tell you what you have to do to make the sale. The only thing better is a signature on the dotted line.

Positively Negative

Everyone loves success – whether it's the accumulation of wealth or the ninth-inning rally. There is something special about victory, about accomplishment and achievement. Winning is positive, and positive is a powerful word and symbol. Positive means certain, correct, and enthusiastic. Positive is good; negative is bad. Yet life is filled with negatives. There is a limited number of perfect lots, a scarcity of great employees, and a buyer pool filled with people we would really rather not have as our customers.

Most people can sell a project with a magnificent vista or a great location. The true challenge is to sell around the obstacles and to construct the right positives to outweigh the almost inevitable negatives. When trying to address negatives, keep in mind these six truths:

1. Some negatives can't be overcome
If some aspect of the house simply doesn't meet buyers' needs, extra positives don't matter. For example, people who are moving because their existing home lacks storage will not buy a house with less storage no matter how much they like it.

2. A negative can only be overcome with a positive
While some negatives can't be overcome, smaller negatives can be overcome by compensatory positives. These positives may already exist (and you simply have to point them out to the client), or you may have to add them.

3. A lower price is not always the best answer to a negative
This is especially true for emotional issues. For example, parents may not like a pond behind their house because they fear for their children's safety. No amount of price reduction will overcome this objection.

4. A bad lot is a *big* negative
A great house on a bad lot typically becomes a bad house. Putting marble in the foyer doesn't make the noisy road go away.

5. One person's trash is another person's treasure

What may be a negative for one person may not be a negative for another. For example, a small lot may be a negative for someone with a growing family, but a positive for an empty-nester or someone looking for low maintenance.

6. Negatives are best eliminated in the planning stage

Common negatives include boring interior layout, inadequate storage, wimpy moldings, dark rooms, and cheap materials. Watch for them.

The person who understands how to overcome obstacles is the person who understands that, sooner or later, every buyer perceives a problem. It's the ability to deal with those negatives that separates the winners from the losers.

How to Deal with a Low-Ball Offer

Everyone, it seems, is looking for a bargain. But some customers are greedy. They look at your house and your selling price, and then they make a low-ball offer and try to steal your work.

Strike One!

When someone makes a low-ball offer, often your first response is to tell them to take a hike. After all, you build houses to make a profit–not to give them away to bottom feeders. But remember to keep your cool: This is about selling a house, not about you or your ego. Before the offer, you had no one interested in buying the house. Now you do. That's progress. All that's left is to negotiate a reasonable price.

Another typical response is to counter with the original price. From a negotiation standpoint, this isn't a good tactic. You're demonstrating that you're inflexible and not very interested in selling. Since you don't move, they don't either, and the "negotiation" reaches an impasse.

A third alternative is to lower the price somewhat in an attempt to move their offer upward. While this may seem a perfectly valid response, it's not effective with a low-ball offer. What it does is establish a negotiation range that's less than you need on the bottom end and less than you want on the top end. If you negotiate within that range, you will most likely end up with a lower offer than you're willing to accept.

Support your price

There's really only one effective response to a low-ball offer and that's to say to the potential buyers something like: "I appreciate your interest but require an offer substantially closer to the asking price."

Support that statement by including all documentation (comps, other offers, recent sales, and so on) that indicates why others are willing to pay your asking price. Stress the benefits: great location, lot, neighborhood, schools, quality construction, etc. Show how the house will provide the quality of life they're looking for, and show that it's fairly valued at the asking price.

Notice what that answer does:

■ It doesn't offend the truly serious buyer who's simply looking for the best deal.

■ It creates a more meaningful negotiation range.

■ It indicates that you are flexible, if they are willing to make a reasonable offer.

■ It puts the ball back in their court for the next round of negotiations.

Finding customers is like looking for a needle in a haystack. You reach in, feel around, and finally find one. Then you pull it out and discover it's a little rusty. So do you throw it away and go looking for another needle – which could also be rusty – or do you try to polish it? Always try to polish the first needle. If you can't, then you throw it away and hunt for another one.

Putting the Custom in Customer

Celebrate Your Success

Sometimes a small shift in attitude makes a big difference in results. Suppose, for example, you have a spec house you really want to get off the books. The interest is cutting into your profits, and you want to clear the way for the next house. Here are two ways to do it:

1. Announce your desperation by giving it away. Slash $10,000 from the sales price, pay the closing costs, throw in a free deck, and increase the sales agent's commission.

2. Celebrate your success. Slash $10,000 from the sales price, pay the closing costs, and throw in a new deck for the lucky customer who helped you reach your goal.

It's all about presentation and perception

The subliminal message in the first scenario says to the buyer: "I'm desperate. My product must not be very good, so please offer less than what the market will bear." The second method, however, says that you've had a banner year and that you want to share some of that success with prospective buyers. Is there any doubt about which message is preferable?

There are two reasons that the celebration tactic works best. First, it keeps you from setting a bad precedent regarding concessions. For example, if you give something away without a specific reason (like an anniversary, Mother's Day, or other event) the customer can come back to you later and demand other concessions. But if you used the celebration tactic and a customer tries to negotiate further, you can reply: "I'm sorry, that was our special anniversary price."

Second, you can put the best face on a situation. Politicians call this spin control. You want the buyer to view the price reduction as a matter of strength, not weakness. This puts you in a better negotiation position in the future.

Every day is a holiday

If you don't have a built-in reason to celebrate, create one. Have regular parties and special events for both clients and employees.

Celebrate St. Patrick's Day, Mardi Gras, Thanksgiving . . . any holiday. Mark the occasion of your 100th or 500th home with a special model and price. Commemorate your company's anniversary with incentives and upgrades.

Create events

Two companies outside the home building industry who capitalize on presentation and perception are The Saturn Corp. and TGI Friday's, the restaurant chain. When you buy a new Saturn, everyone in the show-room comes over to congratulate you. They turn selling a car into an event. At TGI Friday's, your dinner is free on your birthday, and the wait staff comes to your table to sing and congratulate you.

Celebrations are a powerful tool in the building business as well. Just ask The Walt Disney Co., which is no slouch when it comes to marketing. The company's new Florida community is named, simply and appropriately, Celebration.

Everyone loves a good time, and everyone loves to share in the benefits of success. The idea is to make buyers feel they are part of the story – part of why you had a good year and are now in the mood to celebrate.

3
What's Your Message

At Home Builders Network, we talk to builders all over the country. When they need help with marketing, we always ask them "What's your message? Why should someone buy a home from you, rather than your competitor?" Then when we look at their marketing materials, we often find that this message is missing. They don't know what to say, or how to say it.

According to David Olgivy, the legendary advertising man, 80% percent of the impact of your marketing is *what* you say (message) and only 20% is where you say it. So as you begin thinking about improving your marketing, this is place to start.

A good message should have the following characteristics:

■ **Focus on the customer, rather than the builder.** Buyers aren't interested in you. They're interested in what you can do for them.

■ **Sell the benefits, rather than the features.** Features are what the product is. Benefits are what it does for them.

■ **Use emotion effectively.** Remember, buying a new home is an emotional decision.

■ **Sell value, not price.** Selling on price is the fastest way to cut your profits.

■ **Be consistent.** Concentrate on 3 or 4 main benefits and repeat them in all your marketing.

■ **Include a call to action.** Give them a phone number and a reason to call.

"Talk to a man about himself and he will listen for hours."

— Benjamin Disraeli

The 3 M's of Marketing

To improve effectiveness, you have to concentrate on the 3 Ms of marketing: the Message, the Media, and the Means.

The Message

Without a strong message, your marketing is going nowhere, lost in the clutter of competitive claims. So before you do anything else, make sure you have the right message. Build it on the major benefits you provide your customers, those that set you apart from your competition. Go through all your features and turn them into benefits (see page xx). Then pick the top three or four benefits and make that your marketing message.

An important part of the message is your positioning strategy. If everyone else is offering cookie-cutter boxes, you may want to offer semi-custom flexibility.

To be effective your message should have the following characteristics:
Be buyer oriented. Talk about buyers' needs and wants, rather than about you.
Be action oriented. Get prospects to do something – pick up a phone or visit.
Be credible. Avoid glittering generalities like "We're the Best." Don't tell them you're the best, show them. To denote higher quality, for example, show a photo of an elegant moulding or a Corian countertop.

The Media

Once you've developed the message, you need to consistently apply that message to all marketing materials, including brochures, fliers, postcards, and advertising. Sometimes it's helpful to think of marketing as a two-step process: generating leads and closing leads.

Use inexpensive materials, such as flyers and postcards, to generate leads. Use more expensive and more comprehensive materials to generate interest and enthusiasm to buy. Remember, the more work the materials do before a face-to-face meeting, the easier it is to close the sale.

Advertising needs to be consistent, and it has to be frequent. That's why a simple, small ad that appears often in a targeted publication is more

What's Your Message?

effective than a large ad that appears once or twice in a mainstream publication. Try out-of-the-way publications such as medical and professional newsletters or employee newsletters of major companies. When deciding which ones to use, ask yourself: Are the readers of this publication people who can afford and appreciate my product?

The Means

Once you have all your elements in place (message, image, and marketing tools) implement an aggressive marketing program. Set up a budget with a minimum of 1.5% to 2% of gross sales allocated for marketing. This doesn't include sales commissions. It is used for marketing materials, direct mail, advertising, and special events. If you find that your marketing is too effective and you're generating too much business, then be more selective in your client base. Raise your prices and profits or expand production to meet demand.

Remember, the biggest marketing mistake you can make is having a weak message that doesn't speak to your target audience. So take the time to develop a solid message. It will make all the difference.

Creating Customers

No matter how good a builder you are, no matter how good you are at controlling costs, unless someone is willing to buy your product, you're out of business. The first stage in that process is to LOCATE your clients. There are four major phases in locating clients. The first letter of each step spells the word *seek*:

- **S**elect your target
- **E**valuate market needs
- **E**liminate non-buyers
- **K**eep at it (Repetition)

Select your target

The first thing you must decide is "Who is my target buyer?" If you try to be everything to everyone, you end up being nothing to anyone. Since you can't be everywhere, concentrate your firepower where it will do the most good. There are three ways to concentrate: Geographic, Demographic, and Lifestyle. Geographic concentration allows you to minimize your marketing and transportation costs and have a better understanding of your market. Demographic concentration (income, education, age) allows you to better understand and serve the needs of a particular market segment. And Lifestyle concentration allows you to meet the needs of a segment as it ages and its housing needs change. (Segments include singles, couples, married with children, and empty nesters. Each segment has different housing needs.)

Evaluate market needs

Once you know your potential buyers, you need to evaluate their needs and determine if your product meets those needs in a cost-effective way. The important thing here is to understand the difference between needs and wants. Needs are minimum requirements of buyers. Unless they're met, they aren't interested. Wants are benefits which go beyond the minimum needs. Inability to satisfy needs is a deal breaker. But the ability to satisfy the most wants is the deal maker.

Once you understand your market's needs and wants, use that information to drive your marketing effort. The most important rule of marketing is

What's Your Message?

to *sell benefits*, not features. Benefits are what your product does for your customers and how it fulfills their needs. Any marketing that does not focus on benefits is simply a waste of time and money.

Eliminate non-buyers

As important as it is to know who your buyers *are*, it's also important to know who they are *not*. Sales people call this pre-qualification. Before you spend a lot of time with someone, you need to know if he has the desire *and* the ability to buy your product. People may have a strong need for your product, but unless they have the means to buy it, they aren't a customer.

Keep at it (repetition)

Studies have shown that it takes at least 3 "hits" of a marketing message to move someone to action. However, because of the marketing clutter today, people only see one out of every nine messages to which they're exposed. That means you have to expose them to 27 messages to move them to action. Many builders run an ad only two or three times (or less) before they get tired of it and change it. To be effective, you have to repeat your message over and over again.

If you follow this four-step process – *Select* your target, *Evaluate* market needs, *Eliminate* non-buyers, and *Keep* at it – you will discover that you will have located a great many potential customers who previously did not know you existed.

Making a Name for Yourself

The other day I was doing some grocery shopping and I picked up a bag of Lay's barbecue potato chips. These weren't just any barbecue-flavored chip. They were flavored with KC Masterpiece Barbecue Sauce. Right next to those were ranch flavored potato chips, made with Hidden Valley Ranch Dressing. "This is a great example of cross marketing," I thought. Frito-Lay, KC Masterpiece and Hidden Valley must all be owned by the same company. But when I checked the fine print I was wrong. They were entirely separate companies.

Instead, this was the perfect example of leveraging brand-name recognition. Both Frito-Lay and KC Masterpiece spend millions of dollars every year to create awareness and recognition for their products. The consumer knows that KC Masterpiece means quality barbecue sauce. Therefore, any potato chip that uses this superior barbecue sauce is perceived to be superior to one that uses a non-brand "generic" barbecue sauce flavoring. And in the world of marketing, perception is reality.

Create your own brand

You can use this same principle of leveraging brand-name recognition in your own business. As a small builder or contractor you don't have millions of dollars to spend on marketing to create awareness and acceptance. Wouldn't it be nice if you could leverage the millions of dollars national manufacturers spend on their marketing for your own benefit? You can, and there are two ways to do this.

Piggyback recognition

The first way is to decide what national brands you want to use in your building efforts. Yes, a nationally advertised brand of window such as Andersen costs a few dollars more than a "no-name" generic brand, or a brand which has little recognition. But for those few extra dollars, you can gain a quality perception for your entire product which greatly exceeds the small price difference. Consumers perceive certain products as quality products. If you use those quality products in your work, and you let people know you use these quality products, then, by extension, you must be a quality builder. At the least, you'll be perceived as being better than those

What's Your Message?

builders who don't care enough about their houses to use these products.

Once you decide on the products you'll use, let consumers know by including them in your marketing. If you use Kohler plumbing fixtures, for example, you say, "We care enough about the quality of our product that we use Kohler throughout our homes." Even if other builders in the area use the same plumbing fixtures, what can they say – "We use Kohler also"? "Me too" marketing never works.

Use co-op marketing

The second way is to use co-op advertising dollars. These same national companies will actually *pay* you to use their brand names to increase your quality perception. Depending on the particular program, companies will pay up to half the cost of running an ad, or printing a marketing tool, as long as their brand name is prominently featured. They are able to stretch their advertising dollars and ensure brand loyalty, and you get twice as much advertising for the same buck.

To find out how to use co-op advertising dollars, contact your local building materials supplier. Often these national companies have allocated more money for co-op advertising than is being used. They'll tell you what you have to do to qualify for these funds. They may even help you prepare these materials.

Increasing your quality perception by leveraging on national brand name recognition *and* getting paid to do it – that's the best of both worlds, and it sounds like a win/ win situation all around.

Sell the Benefits

The major mistake that builders and contractors make in selling their product is that they tell their customers about the features of the product, but forget to sell the benefits. Features are what a product does. Benefits are what the product does for the client. To communicate benefits, look at your product from the viewpoint of the customer. How does it satisfy their needs? How does it make their life better? What's in it for them?

For example, brick veneer is a feature. The durability, low maintenance, and luxury status of brick is a benefit. The HVAC system is a feature. The energy savings of a high-efficiency HVAC system is a benefit.
Not all benefits are physical or functional. Often these benefits are emotional, financial, and procedural. In selling benefits, remember to sell the total benefits.

By selling benefits, you create a perceived value in the customer's mind. This leads to increased profits in several ways. First, you increase sales. Second, you no longer compete solely on price. People are willing to pay more for a Mercedes than a Geo Metro. It's the same in houses. Home buyers are willing to pay more, provided they perceive they're getting more. By selling benefits, you move your product toward the Mercedes category and away from the Geo Metro.

So what?

There is one surefire way to distinguish features from benefits. Ask yourself: "So what?" If a potential buyer looks at a marketing claim and says, "So what?" then it isn't a benefit. In the words of William James, "A difference, to be a difference, must make a difference."

If you use 5/8-inch drywall, and everyone else uses 1/2-inch drywall, the customer will say, "So what?" That's a feature, but they need to understand that 5/8-inch drywall provides extra sound control and extra fire protection. That's the benefit.

Translating features to benefits

Most features are benefits in disguise. All you have to do is paint the picture in the customer's mind. Here are some ways to translate features into

What's Your Message?

benefits in talking about homes:

Bedrooms. *Feature:* Master bedroom on the first level. *Benefit*: Increased privacy (separation from the children's area) and the greater convenience of one-level living for the parents.

Heating and Cooling. *Feature*: High efficiency heat pump. *Benefit*: Save on energy costs now, and even more in the future as energy prices increase. *Feature*: Zoned temperature controls. *Benefit*: Individual comfort for different temperature preferences.

Siding. *Feature*: Heavy duty vinyl. *Benefits*: Long-lasting beauty, reduced maintenance (no scraping and painting), good weather resistance, trouble free living.

Countertop. Feature: Corian solid surfacing. Benefit: Increased beauty, name recognition, easy maintenance.

Windows. *Feature*: Low-e windows with heat screen. *Benefits*: Reduced glare (comfort), reduced heat gain (energy savings) and reduced UV fading (reduced maintenance).

Eat-in-Kitchen. *Feature*: Island kitchen. *Benefits*: More efficient use of space, a kitchen two can cook in comfortably. *Feature*: Kitchen adjoins breakfast nook and family room. *Benefits*: Family and entertaining convenience, better social interaction.

Take your laundry list of features in your current homes and translate them into benefits that mean something to your buyers. Until you establish the benefit, you haven't created the value.

Sell *All* the Benefits

In marketing their homes, builders understand and emphasize two aspects of their product: the physical and the financial. They know what goes into a house, how it's built, and how much it costs. What they fail to realize is that buyers often have very different reasons for buying a house. If you only sell two of the benefits, you may be missing the opportunity to create a great deal of value in your homes.

In order to help builders compete more effectively, we developed the TPM^2 (Total Product Management and Marketing) concept. According to TPM^2, every product has five attributes. It is the total impact of these attributes that make the product valuable in the customer's mind. These attributes are the **Physical, Functional, Emotional, Financial,** and **Procedural.** To illustrate this concept, look at a very simple product (brick) in terms of it's total product attributes.

1. Physical. What is the product?
A brick is a piece of fired clay, approximately 2 2/3" high, 4" wide, and 8" long. It comes in a variety of colors and textures.

2. Functional. What does it do? How does it do it?
Bricks usually are used for exterior veneer, to keep out rain and wind. Most people feel that brick is a structural element, but that's not usually the case. Sometimes bricks are used for flooring, interior walls, and fireplaces.

3. Emotional. How does it make you feel?
Bricks signify security and status. How brick came to signify status is an interesting story. In early colonial days, bricks were used as ballast in ships. They unloaded the brick in America, and loaded products to ship to England. Since the ship owners had all this extra brick lying around, they used it to build their homes. And since ship owners were wealthy, the homes they built with their cheap brick came to represent status and wealth.

4. Financial. What does it cost?
Brick siding costs more than wood, aluminum or vinyl siding. However, brick can last for a long time. There is much less maintenance than

What's Your Message?

painted wood siding. So the lifetime cost of brick may be equal to or less than that of wood.

5. Procedural. What do I have to do to get it?

The procedural aspects of brick are finding good masons, and ordering the brick. If it's a special brick, how long will it take to get here?

The value of the product is the *sum* of all the attributes. The attributes that are often ignored, such as emotional, functional, and procedural, are often *much* more important than the physical attributes of the product. Buying a home, for example, is a very emotional decision, and the procedural aspects such as getting financing, closing, and customer service, can often make or break the sale.

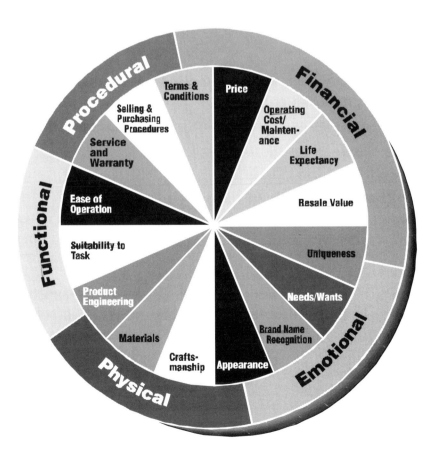

The Value Proposition

Every builder offers his buyer a particular value proposition. These value propositions don't exist in a vacuum. They make a statement about you relative to your competition. But if your value proposition is to work, it must be one that's important to your target buyers, it must be consistent, and it must be credible. Some of these value propositions are:

We give you more at the same price.
We give you the same at a lower price.
We give you more at a lower price.
We give a little less at a much lower price.
We give a lot more for a little more.
We charge a lot more, and we're worth every penny.

What's important to your buyers?

Different target buyers respond differently to different value propositions. You can tell this by looking at where they shop. Wal-Mart shoppers use Value 2: "We give the same (brand names) at a lower price." Nordstrom shoppers use Value 5: "We give you a lot more (better merchandise, better service) for a little more." If your buyers are more quality conscious than price conscious, then your value proposition should reflect that bias.

Where is the competition?

To determine your value proposition you need to know your competitors and their value proposition. Sometimes you can determine that by simply looking at their advertising and marketing. If their value proposition is readily apparent, they have their marketing act together and they're going to be tough competition. It can also mean they may have staked out a value proposition you wanted to use. If everyone claims that "we will not be undersold," no one really benefits.

However, if you're confused after reading your competitor's advertising, that's good. It means their potential buyers will also be confused. It also allows you to choose the value proposition that makes the most sense to you, allows you the most profits and has the broadest consumer appeal.

You may want to visit your competitor's homes to determine the validity and credibility of their value proposition. Have a friend visit, pick up their materials and ask about their home building philosophy. What are they claiming and, more importantly, how are they substantiating that claim? How do they claim to be superior to the competition?

Make it credible

Once you've determined your competitor's value proposition, you need to decide yours. If you're both offering the same proposition, find dramatic ways to make your claim more credible. If you're offering a different value proposition, find ways to demonstrate that value to the buyer in a memorable way.

The benefits you offer to establish your value proposition must be concrete and specific. Generalities and unsubstantiated claims about "quality" are simply discounted. You can set yourself apart from your competition through better design, better location, better materials and craftsmanship, better service and procedures, more curb appeal, better indoor/outdoor living, using brand-name components, and using interior focal points to create the "wow" and excitement that sells homes. Use any or all of these to substantiate your claims of value.

Be consistent

Once you've chosen a value proposition, use it consistently. Nothing is worse than confusing the buyer with inconsistent messages and contradictory information. When buyers are confused, they tend *not* to make a decision. Many builders don't even know they're sending an inconsistent message, even when the message changes every time they run an ad or when they shift perspective. For example, if your value proposition stresses quality, rather than price, but your marketing talks about all the free things you're offering to induce them to buy, that's a mixed message. In effect, you're sending a Wal-Mart message to a Nordstrom shopper, and undermining your value proposition.

The value proposition can be a powerful marketing tool if you use it to set yourself apart from the competition, use it consistently and use it to establish credibility. Remember, it's value, not just price, that consumers are looking for.

4 Ways to Think About Price

When talking about how to compete, custom builders often focus on price. They constantly tell me "They're killing me on price." These builders miss the bigger picture. People who sell products focus on the aspects they know best. For builders, this is usually physical (what it's made of and how it's put together) and financial (what's the price). If price becomes an issue, here are four ways to put it into context for your customer,

1. Price is relative to quality

A Mercedes costs more than a Geo for a reason. The next time your customers get hung up about price, ask them what kind of car they drive. Why don't they drive a Geo Metro? This open-ended question tells them your product corresponds to their value system.

2. Price is relative to time

In buying a new home, the critical factor is the monthly payment. Adding $1,000 in construction costs at 9 percent adds $8.05 to the monthly payment. So the issue isn't whether the customer can afford the $1,000, it's whether they can afford $8.05 a month. Help them see the big picture.

Initial price is only one aspect of the total cost. Some things, such as better windows, may have a higher initial price, but may actually save money over the life of the house, and add significantly to resale value. It would therefore have a lower total cost. If the builder can show that total costs are lower, then a higher initial price can be justified.

3. The lowest price isn't always the best price

Sometimes it isn't even the lowest price. It just seems that way. A better grade window that is pre-primed or clad has a higher initial price than a standard window. However, by the time you install it and paint it, etc. the cost may be quite close. Pre-hung door units have a higher price than individual components. But by the time you add the cost on job-site installation, the savings are negligible or nonexistent.

4. Compare apples to apples

Not only can't you compare a Mercedes to a Geo you can't even compare a Mercedes to a Lexus. Even if they cost the same, there are strong emotional differences. No two custom homes are alike either. Even if two builders bid the same plans, their quality and interpretation will differ. Those differences are your competitive edge.

Remember price is only one characteristic of a home's value. To many people, it's not even the most important one. When people want to talk about price, focus on the other characteristics. If you do that, you'll find you'll be better able to compete and to justify a reasonable price for your product.

What's Your Message?

Selling Procedure

One of the best selling cars in America today is the Saturn. It's also the car with the highest customer satisfaction. It's a nice car, reasonably priced. But one of the major reasons for its success is that Saturn is very smart about how it sells it products – it's what we call *selling procedure.*

Buying a new car is usually not fun. You have to hassle with the dealer to get the best price, and then you find out later that someone you know got an even better deal. Saturn decided to take the hassle out of buying. Sales people quote you their lowest price right at the beginning. If the car is what you want and you're happy with the price, you buy the car. No hassle. Saturn also goes out of its way to get you the car you want and arrange financing. When you pick up the car, the entire staff gathers round, shakes your hand and congratulates you on your new purchase. They make you feel special and follow this up with personal phone calls, surveys and excellent service. They use this no-hassle policy very effectively in their marketing. Saturn is a "new kind of car company," they tell everyone. Now that's selling procedure.

Like buying a car, buying a home is not always a wonderful experience. After the initial euphoria of making the decision wears off, there's financing to arrange, materials to select, colors to pick. There are draws to approve and change orders to be signed and paid. What could be an exciting and satisfying experience can often make the buyer – and builder – feel like they are being nibbled to death by ducks.

Make it easy

Selling procedure is an often-overlooked aspect of marketing. Builders concentrate on the sticks and bricks, the design and the price but don't understand that the process of buying is often the most negative aspect of the product. Smart builders streamline and systematize their procedures to make decisions and paperwork as easy as possible. They have prearranged financing and easy-to-fill-out customer preference sheets. They keep samples of the most commonly selected materials in the office so buyers don't have to run from store to store, making their choices.

Simplify decisions

Smart builders try to prepackage selections into families of components, colors and materials that go together. They may hire an interior designer to pull together these selections into "designer-coordinated" options. They know that the more work they do ahead of time, the less work the buyer has to do and the smoother the procedure will go.

Selling procedure doesn't mean you have to be a doormat for your customers. Even though Saturn goes out of its way for its customers, it does not negotiate price. The procedures are simple and they're the same for everyone. To gain a competitive advantage, however, you have to improve your procedures – and you have to let your potential buyers know about them. If you work hard to make their life easier, tell them so.

If you can ease the buyer's anxiety and reduce the hassle of buying a home, you've given them a major reason to come to you, rather that your competition. That's selling procedure.

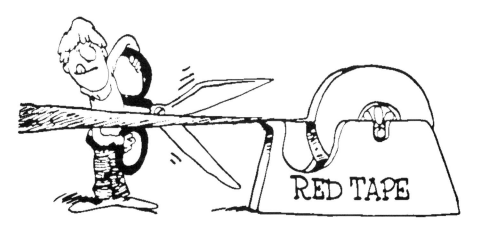

Tell 'em a Story

Every day, we're bombarded by dozens of marketing messages. We simply filter out most of them – they never enter our consciousness. But as builders creating a marketing message, we must make a positive and believable impression – and a message that won't be filtered out by the prospective buyer. How? By providing concrete details and human-interest stories.

An ad that says, "We're the best" is generally discounted. But an ad that says "We're No. 2 – we try harder" gets noticed because it's specific and provides a benefit to the reader. And remember that famous Rolls Royce ad that focused on how quiet the car was: "At 60 miles per hour, the loudest sound you hear is the ticking of the clock." That's a concrete detail readers can relate to. They can imagine themselves inside the car, the clock ticking away, and everything else whisper quiet. (By the way, when the Rolls Royce engineers read the ad, their comment was, "Yes, we must do something about that clock.")

Get specific about benefits

Don't get lazy and tell your story by using glittering generalities: "We're the best! Our prices are fantastic! All our customers are satisfied!" It takes effort and imagination to create specifics that reinforce your message. Suppose, for example, that two of your major selling features are the organized way you build and the excellent communication between clients and builder. To make that message believable, include details of the process – the weekly progress reports, the prearranged selection schedule – and how that process will make their life easier.

Builders often use specific facts but don't tell us what they mean. For example, you may use an oversized water heater (or two water heaters). If you tell the buyers that you use an 80 gallon heater, they probably have no idea how big their present water heater is, and whether 80 is more or less than is expected. You have to tell them the 80 gallon heater ensures a steady supply of hot water when they're in the shower.

Use specifics to sell quality

The problem with selling quality is that everyone claims to have it. You can, however, use specific quality indicators to convince your reader indirectly. If you use a particular brand of window or plumbing fixture that is recognized for its quality, use that brand name in your advertising. If you use exceptional building or finishing details, use a picture that shows the details, and then call attention to them in a caption. Point out, for example, that "The quality of an ABC home is evident in the finishing detail."

Use human interest

People love to hear stories. The Hallmark cards commercials are so effective because they tell a highly emotional story in 60 seconds. A builder can use the same technique by telling stories about real life people – their needs and wants – and how he was able to solve their problems. Two major concerns of custom buyers, for example, are cost overruns and construction delays. Tell them some good stories about how those things can get out of control and the steps you take to manage them to your customers' benefit. Provide concrete details in the story to make them believable.

It takes more effort to base your marketing message on concrete detail and human-interest stories. However, your message will be much more effective and will result in higher sales, higher profits and greater customer satisfaction. And that sounds like good marketing to us.

What Builders Want from Salespeople

First and foremost, builders want results. They don't want promises or potential or excuses. The smart builders also want someone who can be a part of the management team, who can provide valuable information on buyer needs and wants and how to reach those buyers. Here are seven things that builders are looking for:

1. Intelligent salespeople who can sell value, not just price. If you cut the price low enough, anyone can sell a home. Real salespeople are those that can create value in the mind of the consumer so that the builder can realize a decent profit.

2. Better sales. Not all buyers are created equal. Some buyers lack the resources, and other buyers are simply more trouble than they are worth. The good salesperson puts his priority with the higher quality buyers.

3. More sales. As long as the builder is making a good profit on each home, the more sales he makes, the more profit he makes. Increased sales are the engine that drives growth.

4. Market feedback on existing products. A good salesperson acts as the eyes and the ears of the builder. They can tell builders what works and doesn't work about the current product.

5. Input on future design. Professional salespeople have a good feel for what particular needs and wants are driving the market. And they get this information from the best possible source . . . . asking potential clients directly.

6. Realistic expectations. Salespeople sometimes try to close a sale by promising the buyer anything. Good salespeople don't make promises they can't keep, and don't create unrealistic expectations that will come back to haunt the builder later.

What's Your Message?

7. Team loyalty. The builder is looking for someone who can work to further the builder's long-range goals. This means understanding and incorporating the builders procedures and philosophy. It means looking out for the builder's bottom line, and taking pride in the builder's products.

What do salespeople want?

Like builders, salespeople also want results. However, they realize that many of the factors of success lie outside their control. What they want from the builder are the tools and strategies that make their life easier, and lead to the success and results they crave.

1. Factors of success. If you have a great product at a great location at a great price, even a mediocre salesperson can be successful. On the other hand, even a great salesperson will struggle on a project that's overpriced, poorly designed, or poorly located. Professional salespeople want input into the factors that affect their success, such as product design, pricing strategy, and marketing.

2. Access to builder. If salespeople have access to the builder, they can often influence those factors of success. They want to be part of the team, and develop a reciprocal sense of loyalty.

3. Reward for outstanding success. In order to encourage outstanding performance, compensation for salespeople should be tied to the profit goals of the builder, not simply sales.

Good salespeople are hard to find. So are good builders. And the best ones are those who understand the needs and expectations of each other, and then strive to meet those needs.

Profit Sensitive Compensation

The most fundamental form of incentive for sales people is commission. Sell a lot, make a lot. Sell nothing, make nothing. Yet even though this incentive program appears to be quite logical, it is, in reality, tragically flawed. The hidden defect of the system lies in the fact that it is totally unrealistic in regards to builder profits.

Suppose that you pay a 1% commission. A full price sale of a $200,000 house results in a commission of $2,000. Writing up the same contract with $2,000 worth of concessions (here comes that free deck again) results in a commission of $1,980. Where's the incentive to fight for the last $2,000? In fact, the system gives every reason to write the contract at $198,000. Why would anyone risk a commission of $1,980 for an extra $20.

This thinking is not designed to malign salespeople or imply that they don't try to represent the builder to the best of their ability. Nevertheless, as managers we would be remiss to create a system that encourages the price concessions we are trying so hard to avoid. Remember, a $2,000 concession on a $200,000 house can reduce the net profit by 20-25%.
So how do you deal with this issue? One possible solution is what we call Profit Sensitive Compensation™. It's based on the concept that to change people's behavior, you need to reward behavior you want to encourage, and punish behavior you want to diminish. When they sell a home at full sales price, they earn a bonus in addition to their commission. When they sell for less than the sales price, a significant part of that reduction comes out of their commission.

Here's an example of how such a system might work. Pick a point one percent below your full-sales price ($198,000). If the salesperson sells it at that price, they get their full commission based on that price ($1,980). If they sell it at $200,000, they get their full commission on $198,000 **plus** 25% of the difference between the cutoff price and the sales price. That's a $500 bonus ($2,480) – a good incentive to sell for full price. If they sell for less than the cutoff price, their commission is reduced by 25% of the difference between the cutoff price and the final sales price. At $196,000 this would result in a reduction of their sales commission by $500 (to

$1,480). That's an incentive to sell the home on value, rather than take the easy way and sell on price.

The downside risk is a little scary to the salesperson. If they brought you a contract for $10,000 less than the asking price, they would end up earning no sales commission at all (actually, they'd owe *you* money). So you may want to limit the downside risk to 50% of commission. That's still a very powerful incentive, and very sensitive to profitability.

If you don't have a problem with salespeople selling on price, then your present system must be working just fine. If you do have a problem, teach them to think in terms of profits and value, rather than price.

By using Profit Sensitive Compensation, you provide a powerful incentive for your salespeople to protect your profits. After all, the profits they save may be their own.

Surf's Up

Some industry experts believe that the Internet is "The Answer," a magical tool that will change everyone's life and everyone's business. Some view the Internet as just one more overhyped and overused technological gimmick, the latest in a never-ending series of constantly changing "improvements" that are costly, require lengthy setup time and have steep learning curves. The truth is somewhere in the middle.

The Internet of today is a fast-growing multimedia opportunity. It is used by only a modest segment of the population (10 to 30 million people, depending on whose data you believe). Yet this market segment has some very interesting characteristics. Most are under 45 years old. The vast majority (80% or more) are college graduates. The average income is in the top 10% of the population. There is probably no finer opportunity today for niche marketing to this group of young, educated, upscale buyers.

The first step is to create your presence on the Internet. This is called a *home page* (no pun intended). You can create your home page yourself, using inexpensive software created for this purpose, or find a service that can create and maintain your presence for you. Some on-line services, such as CompuServe, allow users to create a home page that is easily accessible to other CompuServe subscribers. But for real Internet access, you need to find an Internet provider.

What should it cost?

Prices for this service vary widely – from thousands of dollars for multi-page interactive sites, to a few hundred dollars or less for a simple layout. You usually pay a monthly maintenance fee to store your site on the Internet provider's computer. These service providers are growing by leaps and bounds; finding one near you shouldn't be too hard.

It's all about information

People usually come to the Internet looking for information. So give them the information they're looking for – about housing, location of your communities, type of construction you do, etc. A good start is to create an electronic version of your benefit brochure. Use pictures (color scans) of some of the homes you've built and of the construction process. On-line is one place where it costs no more to go full-color.

There are a lot of boring messages on the Internet and you don't really help yourself by adding to the clutter. Make your message short, simple, and to the point. And *always* provide a call to action, a way and a reason for the prospect to get in touch with you. Offer to send additional information about your homes, services, and communities.

Think of the Internet as electronic Yellow Pages – people come looking for you because they are interested in your product. Make it easier for them to find you by registering your page with the major search engines (Yahoo, etc.). Your Internet provider can register you for a fee. In addition, publicize your Internet address by placing it in all your print advertising, and on letterhead, business cards and correspondence.

The amount of dollars necessary to have a presence is not particularly significant and even if your site doesn't generate a lot of business at first, being on-line is a status symbol which tells your potential customers that you are a technologically savvy individual. For a builder – a technically oriented profession in the minds of most consumers – this is a *good* thing.

The Internet is *not* the answer to all your marketing needs but it's becoming more important to businesses and it costs very little to get online and maintain a presence. The Internet is about access to information, not a place for a blatant sales pitch. However, information selling is highly effective for big-buck purchases such as home buying.

What's Your Message?

What Are You Waiting for?

How to use Internet marketing to improve sales and profits

I'm not the first guy on the block to rush out and try some new technology. Several years ago, I was badly burned when I installed a new version of Windows, and I lost my entire hard drive due to software incompatibility. Now I wait until the second version (at least) of any new software. I let other people work out the bugs first. I want solutions that work.

So a year ago, when a builder asked me if they needed to be on the Internet, I said, "Not yet. It's a great idea whose time has not yet come." But I've changed my mind. Now is the time to get on the Internet, and here are the reasons why.

It's affordable

Where else can you provide information to consumers about your company day or night, for $20 a month? That's what you pay with some Internet providers for your connect fee. Yes, you might have to pay a little bit to set up your web site. But no other medium allows you to deliver a four-color brochure about your company, day or night, to anyone who requests that information. Just think what FedEx would charge for the same service.

It's fast

Consumers get the information when they want it: *Now!* The alternative: they call your office the next day, you put the information in an envelope, and then they wait for the mail. Faster response on your part leads to faster decision making on the part of the consumer. That's faster than FedEx.

It's flexible

When you want to change the information on your web site, all you have to do is edit it. You can add to it, and update information daily. Try that with a four-color brochure.

It's on demand

The greatest advantage of web publishing is that it provides information on-demand, in a non-intrusive manner. Most marketing efforts are ignored

What's Your Message?

because they try to provide information we don't want, at a time when we don't want it. When the consumer goes looking for the information, they're much more receptive, and much more likely to act on it.

The demographics are great

It's true that not everyone is on the Internet. However, the people who are on the Internet are the people you want to do business with. They are upper-income, highly educated, more sophisticated buyers. In addition, there are lots of them. Over 50 million people in the U.S. can now access the Internet. It took just 2 years to reach that level of penetration. In contrast, it took television 10 years and radio 50 years to reach those levels.

Doing it right

There's a right way and a wrong way to develop a web site. The wrong way is to hire someone to develop a site for you – who doesn't understand your business – and let them make all the decisions about content and format. The right way is to think through what information consumers want and need, and then work with a site provider to develop that information.

Remember, a web site is all about information. If you provide the information people want, they'll visit your site and keep coming back.

Information Sells

Many builder web sites that I've seen are a waste of time and effort. They are basically an "ego trip" for the builder, so they can tell customers and friends that they're technologically hip and up-to-date. They treat the web site as if it were just another marketing piece, full of hype and glittering generalities. They miss the golden opportunity to fill the potential buyer's need for information.

Information selling

The Internet is fundamentally different from other marketing tools. People come to the Internet for information, not a sales pitch. If you don't give them the information you're looking for, they'll go somewhere else. So what information are they looking for? It all depends on the person looking. If they're actively looking to buy a home, they may want to cut quickly to the relevant purchase information: What's available, where, at what price. If you're a custom builder, they may want information about what kind of homes you build, what the process is like, and ideas they can incorporate into their own home. If they're just "curious" then they want information about home design and the building process in general.

What they *don't* want is hype and glittering generalities. Save the sales pitch for the sales office. On the web, your approach should be low-key and information packed. Give them lots of specifics, lots of pictures of current products, and make the information meaningful. Think of it as customer education, rather than customer sales. Haven't you always wished you could spend more time with customers educating them on what to expect, and how to make the most of the process? Here's your chance, without spending a lot of personal time doing it.

Organization

The wonderful thing about the web is that it is "self-directed." Since different people want different information, you need to organize your web site so that they can retrieve the information they're looking for, without wading through information they don't care about. For example, a typical site for a builder might include separate pages for Process, Product, Locations. It might also include a page for "Design tips" that people might want to include in their present homes. It might include a section on "How to select a builder" written by an outside expert. None of these pages should try to be a hard-hitting sales piece. Instead, the idea is to increase the potential buyer's comfort level with you as a builder. Then, when they're ready to build or buy, you're the one they think of.

Keep it simple

You can have as many pages as you like, but you should have one major message per page. Subordinate pages should provide reinforcement and detail to support that message.

Make it easy

Provide links on each page that make it easy for the user to navigate around your site. Don't confuse the user with busy layouts or extraneous information.

Make it visually interesting

Just as in brochures, the quality of the images reflects the quality of your product. If it's not a good photograph, don't put it on the web. Be careful, however, about using large graphics that can take a long time to upload. A better approach is to place a small graphic that the user can click on to enlarge. And don't forget captions. These are marvelous devices that tell the reader the meaning of the photo.

By concentrating on buyer information needs and organizing your site to provide easy access, you can create a powerful tool for buyer education and create a real presence that can lead to increased sales.

Your Internet Message

While the purpose of an Internet site is different than that of a marketing brochure, they do have several things in common. You want to create interest on the part of the viewer by presenting the information they're looking for, in a lively way, and lead them to request more information and a personal contact.

The most important thing to remember is that this is about your clients, not about you. They really could care less about how wonderful you are, unless it relates in some way to their own wants and needs. This is where most web sites fall down. They try to tell the viewer everything about them, instead of translating that information into consumer benefits. While the content of the web site may vary depending on your message, each web site is organized in a similar fashion, with a home page, content pages, and a call to action. Remember that messages are conveyed not only with words, but with pictures and organization.

Home Page

This is the first page that viewers will see when they access your site. If it isn't exciting, well organized, and easy to use, you will have lost them. Therefore, keep this page as simple as possible. Show a nice picture of a recent home. Include a navigation bar that shows all the different content pages they can visit directly from the home page. If you have a one sentence statement that sums up your business philosophy, this is the place for it. This is *not* the place for small type or cluttered layout. Keep it simple and inviting, and induce them to visit your other pages.

Content pages

The content pages are where the bulk of your message will go. Again, the major rule is don't try to put too much on any one page.

Do you want to build or buy a house? If you're a custom builder, you would focus on all the elements that go into building a home, including design, estimating, financing, construction, and building. You could also discuss the criteria of how to select a builder. (Of course, those criteria somehow exactly match your profile. Surprise.) If you're a production

What's Your Message?

builder focus on the benefits and advantages of your product, and how readers should evaluate a home purchase. Include a small rating form.

Design makes the difference. Show several homes that are typical of the ones you build. If you have a plan portfolio, or do extensive modifications of predetermined plans (semi-custom), here's the place to include these plans. If you can interpose photos of constructed homes from these plans, so much the better.

What to expect. This is a great opportunity to tell a story of the building of a home from start to finish. Think of it as a slide show, with captions alongside each photo taking a family from design, to foundation, to framing, to close-in, to inspection, to closing.

Welcome to the neighborhood. If you build in a given community (or several) here's the place to show what it's like to live there. Show streetscapes with nice landscaping, talk about nearby community amenities like parks, schools, etc. If you want, show a site plan including lots that are built or sold.

Call to action

Before they leave your site, make sure they've obtained all the information they need. Have a page where they can request additional information; and leave their name, address, phone number and e-mail address. If you develop a good e-mail list, you can ask their permission to send them additional information in the future.

A good Internet site is a very cost-effective marketing investment. But, as with all marketing, it all depends on the message.

4
Building a Better Mousetrap

I t's impossible to overestimate the effect that good architectural design can have on your business. I was recently in a new development that had two builders side by side. Both were considered good builders, used good materials, and had good craftsmanship. The size of the homes and the prices were comparable. Both houses were attractive from the outside. But the minute you walked inside, you felt a difference. One of the houses "felt right." The spaces were warm and inviting. The builder had added visual excitement where it would make a difference. Circulation was smooth and efficient. The overall feeling was that of delight. The other house was large and impressive, but the spaces felt uncomfortable. Some of the spaces were too large and too high ... you rattled around inside them. In some spaces, they had created interior volume using shed ceilings that soared to one side of the room, leaving the person inside with an uneasy feeling. Traffic flow was less efficient. The result: slower sales. How much was the better design worth? In terms of faster sales and higher profits, it was worth an incredible amount. Builders who use tired floor plans to save a few bucks are shooting themselves in the wallets.

When we consult builders on how to reposition themselves to be more competitive, we usually suggest they start with product redesign. Why? Because it's quick, it's relatively inexpensive, and it has an immediate impact on perceived value. When a builder is good, one of his worst competitors isn't other builders, but similar houses he built three to five years ago. By changing the design, you eliminate that problem.

If you want the world to beat a path to your door, you'd better start improving your own mousetrap now.

"Architecture is the art of how to waste space."
— Philip Johnson

Increasing Sales Through Better Design

If you are in a healthy market, but find that there's too much price competition, then the problem may be simply that your product (home design) is not as exciting as it could be. Creating or finding exciting designs that meet buyer needs and wants and that are cost-effective to build is one of the most challenging aspects of the building business.

"That's what buyers want"

Often builders justify their current design by saying "That's what the market wants. That's what sells in this market." Sometimes, however, that just means that everyone else's plans are as bad as yours, and the buyer doesn't have a choice.

How do you know that's what they want?

Builders assume that if a particular model sells, it must be what people really want. But there are many factors that go into a buying decision, such as price, location, and competition. People can't buy what they don't see. To find out what they want, you have to *ask them*. You can do this as part of the sales process, or in a focus group to determine buyer preferences of a particular market group.

Different strokes for different folks

Every market segment has different needs and wants. The home that works for a growing family may not work for empty nesters. As lifestyle, income, and ages change, needs and wants also change. Remember, the product must be tailored to the needs of a particular market group, and (for custom builders), to the particular individual. They aren't cookie-cutter people. So don't give them cookie-cutter solutions.

How do you find good plans?

Builders often use the same plans over and over simply because they haven't found a good source for new design ideas. Sometimes builders try to act as their own designers, without the necessary skill or talent. This is

Building a Better Mousetrap

particularly dangerous with exterior details and elevations, where first impressions are critical.

Find a good designer

Good local designers are not only sources of good design, they're sources of good clients. If the designer is approached by a client directly, they often recommend a good builder. However, make sure the architect is easy to work with, understands cost-effective construction, and has experience in the housing market you specialize in. It's better to find a national designer who knows good design, than settle for a mediocre local designer.

Local designers are also useful for modifying existing plans. They can be a valuable part of your building team, without adding overhead.

Find a good plan service

Good plan services provide affordable, buildable plans at a fraction of the cost of a custom design. In addition, you know ahead of time that the design has some market appeal. The good plan services offer complete customization services. If you want to change a dimension of a plan, or add some new features, the plan service should be able to accommodate your needs for a reasonable price. Be careful, however. There's a *lot* of bad design in home plan services. Carefully review the plans and select the ones you believe are winners; then run these by other people for their comments. Include past buyers and individuals who are similar to your targeted buyers.

Pay a little more for good design

Just as you don't want your buyers to make purchase decisions based solely on price, you don't want to evaluate design based on its cost.

Good design may cost a little more up front in design fees and the added cost of appealing details, but it saves many times that additional cost through good market appeal and cost-effective construction.

Love at First Sight

Buying a new home is primarily an emotional experience. Yes, we justify it as an investment, but the reason we buy one home instead of another often has to do with those intangible tugs on the heart strings as we gaze from the curb for the first time, and as we open the door and step into the interior.

So how do you create that emotional appeal? Falling in love with a house is similar to falling in love with a person. Think of the things that attract you to members of the opposite sex: face, proportion, personality, and the way they present themselves. It's the same with houses.

Architectural style

There's an old saying that "beauty is skin deep." When falling in love, however, you often don't get past that initial skin-deep reaction. In architecture, that skin-deep beauty is called architectural style. Styles are interchangeable. You can use the same floor plan and create a classical, craftsman, Victorian, or Tudor style home. All you have to do is change some of the basic architectural elements. What is important isn't the particular style, but that the house *have* some style. A home that doesn't use the decorative elements that are deeply buried in our subconscious minds is missing the opportunity to connect with the buyer on an emotional level.

Proportion

In architecture, this is called *massing*. It has to do with the different elements of the house, and how they relate to each other. A house that's too high or too long or too flat is an ugly house. A related issue is *articulation,* the way the house presents interesting variation in projecting elements. A boring box has little articulation. A two-story home with an projecting entryway and a gable-on-gable roof has more articulation. A T-shaped floor plan with the family room in the extending wing has even more articulation. People generally like interesting variation in elevations.

Personality

The personality of the home is reflected in the interior floor plan and how the different rooms relate to each other. Homes that are easy to get along with have smooth circulation, light-filled rooms, and comfortable spaces. You can tell the personality of a home the minute you walk through the door. Some homes are uncomfortably pretentious, with spaces that are too big and awkwardly arranged. Some homes are chopped up and claustrophobic, with long narrow hallways and spaces that are all separated from each other. And some homes are warm and inviting, with surprising special spaces that create delight. These houses are designed not just to impress, but to function efficiently.

Presentation

Just as dress, makeup, or hairstyle can enhance attractiveness, interior details can make a lasting impression. This is the art of creating "Memory Points" – special spaces and details that the buyer will remember and refer to long after the visit to the home. In remembering your home, you want them to say … "Oh yes, that was the home with the family room that projected into the outdoors," or "You mean the home with the wonderful kitchen with the curved island." Try to create memory points in all the major spaces – entry, kitchen, family room, master bedroom.

It's not enough to build a nice house at a good price. You have to build a house they can fall in love with at first sight, and continue to fall in love with again and again.

Balancing Perceived Value

No matter how beautiful a design solution may be, if the buyer can't afford it, or the builder can't recover his costs, it's not a good solution. Every design detail in the home should be evaluated in terms of what it adds to the cost versus what it adds to the benefits. Look for ways to eliminate costs and simplify construction without taking away from the perceived benefits.

For example, suppose you are selling an upscale home, and the plans call for a circular stairway, costing $4,000. One alternative would be to replace the stairway with a straight run. The cost is $400. You save $3,600. However, a straight stairway does not have nearly the emotional appeal of a curved stairway. You may have lowered the overall perceived value of the home by more than you saved.

So how do you maximize the emotional appeal, while keeping the costs reasonable? One solution is an L-shaped or U-shaped stair with one or more landings. You could also add a fancy newel post and railing detail. Now you have an emotionally exciting stairway, but it only costs you $800. It may not have all the emotional appeal of a curved stairway, but it's close. You can then take the $3,200 you saved on the stairway and either reduce the price *or* put that $3,200 where it can really make an emotional difference. For example a better entry door, fancier sinks in the master bath, upgraded countertops, or a better grade of cabinet. All of a sudden, the perceived value has risen throughout the entire home.

Every home has a perceived value range. All the components within that home must be consistent with that range. There are two ways you can violate this rule: by overbuilding, or underbuilding.

For example, you would never put a $10,000 media room in a $100,000 starter home. The customer might like the media room, but they aren't willing to pay for it. In this case, profits are reduced by the amount of the extra, but unpaid for, features. On the other hand, you don't want to put cheap linoleum in the foyer of a $300,000 move-up home. Potential buyers will look at that and think that the entire house is poorly built. In this case, the profits are reduced by the difference between the lower selling price, if it sells at all, and the savings.

For each component, there is a range of customer acceptance. If you fall below the range, in even one small aspect, you create a negative image that clouds the entire product.

You can also err in the other direction by vastly exceeding the range of acceptance. As a result, you spend too much time, energy, or money on something that the customer is unwilling to pay for. Balancing the perceived value for each component requires thought and effort. When you examine your product with an eye toward identifying areas that fall above or below the acceptable range you can quickly pinpoint problems that must be solved.

The graph below shows a builder who has fallen below the acceptable lower limit in selecting appliances and has exceeded the upper limit for roofing, intercom, and plumbing. This builder may have installed a wood shake roof when a heavyweight composition shingle would suffice. For the appliances, he may have selected the wrong brand, or, depending on the price range of the house, may have omitted a trash compactor or a built-in microwave.

By evaluating the relative perceived value of the components of the home, you can avoid underbuilding or overbuilding, and maximize the total value of the home.

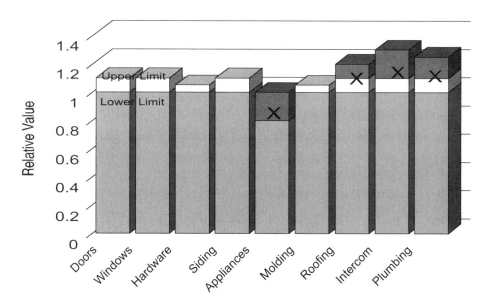

Spec for Success

Some builders are strictly production builders – they don't want the hassles of custom building. Others are custom builders – they don't want the risk of building on speculation. However, even custom builders should consider building some houses on spec. Here's why.

To make a profit
If done right, under the right market conditions, spec homes can yield good profits. They can usually be built faster and with less hassle.

So buyers can see your product
A good spec can be your model home. Many builders start on the next spec as soon as they sell one. This is especially true if you don't have furnished models or want to use a spec house to show a different plan.

To increase exposure
A good spec can get you exposure through Realtors or a parade of homes. To get publicity, a home must be distinctive and have news interest. But don't go overboard: You still want to make a profit.

To minimize hassles
Cutting down on time spent with clients is one of the best reasons to build on spec. As long as you make timely and reasonable decisions, dealing with yourself can be a lot easier than dealing with a client.

To balance production
New custom homes often don't come along exactly when you'd like them to. By building custom and spec, you can keep your crews busy when you don't have a custom home, and you can slack off on spec homes when the custom side is busy.

To sell to a time-sensitive market
Some people can't wait for a custom home to be built. They want a home now. This can also help you with Realtor referrals.

To appeal to buyers afraid of the custom process

Some people can't envision what a home will look like until they're standing in a finished space. These people are afraid of the custom-home process, and specs are the only way to reach them.

Dangers of spec homes

Despite their advantages, specs can present real risks. If the market collapses, you may be stuck with an unsold home. And if the spec business in your area is quite competitive, you may not be able to get the same profits you can get in custom building. Spec homes also can take more time and energy than they give back in profit. When you build a custom home, the customer makes most of the decisions. When you build a spec home, you make those decisions. If you know what you want, this is easy. If not, it can be an ordeal.

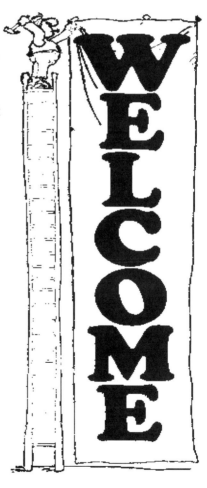

The greatest danger of spec homes is building a monument to your own ego. You may begin thinking of the home as "my" home and put in features the market won't pay for. Have a typical buyer in mind (other than yourself) when planning a spec home.

To avoid these pitfalls, let caution be your guiding principle. Build only enough specs to keep your risk in check.

If you can build efficiently, with an existing crew and a plan firmly in mind, you can reap the benefits of building spec homes.

Price Points, Product Mix, and Lot Premiums

Ever wonder why most things cost less than whole dollar amounts? Why something is priced at $19.95 instead of $20? Is a nickel really that important? The answer, strangely enough, is yes. An item priced just under $20 is perceived to be a better value than one priced at or over that amount. And in marketing, perception is reality.

The same is true of housing. A house priced at $149,900 is perceived to be a better value than one priced at $150,000. In addition, a price that is not rounded to a nice even number is regarded as more precise: $150,000 sounds like a number you pulled out of a hat; $149,900 sounds like a price you worked hard to determine.

Price, price, price

With all the talk about niche, it is easy to lose sight of the importance of product mix and price range. Granted, the price of a new house is determined in part by its location. But to get the most out of a location, you need to create the right array of product with specific focus on psychological price points. Here are the key issues to consider:

■ A good product line has three to five specific home types, each tailored to a specific buyer profile. Thus, if a neighborhood calls for houses in the $150,000 to $175,000 range, you should have a model for a family with two professionals that includes a study and an option for an extra bedroom or office; a model for a family with two or three young kids (four bedrooms, master bedroom up); and one for a slightly older buyer with teenage kids and bad knees (master bedroom down). The market today demands responsiveness to what each buyer *needs* and *wants*.

■ Since it's usually easier to sell up than down (although it's best to do both), make sure to have models priced at important psychological barriers. For the case described here, models at $149,900, $159,900, and $174,900 would be ideal. A traffic generator at $139,900 might be great, depending on the area and market perceptions. It might not be your best seller, but it will bring in people for your sales force to close.

■ Evaluate all the lots you control. Place the largest practical premium on the best lots and smaller premiums on about half the lots. Use at least part of the extra revenue the premiums produce to lower the base price on the least attractive lots. This will help create product for a wider array of buyers. You now have something for the "look honey, it's $10,000 less" crowd and for those looking for quality or prestige ("for $8,000 more, of course I want a view of the woods").

The purpose of using price points, product mix, and lot premiums is to stimulate strong buyer interest early and build critical mass for the project as quickly as possible. Use buyer perception of value to help create that demand.

Master Bedroom: Up or Down?

Around the country, more and more home buyers are looking for a home with the master bedroom on the main level. In a way, this was quite predictable. As the baby boomers grow older and begin thinking about retirement, they know they may not be able to go up and down stairs for the rest of their lives. A master bedroom down design gives them the convenience of one-level living, combined with the cost savings of a two-level design.

One-level living

One-level ranch style housing has always had a certain appeal to a segment of the population. Unfortunately, a one-level house costs approximately 15% more per square foot to build than a comparable two-story house. You have more foundation and roof per square foot. In addition, one-level homes require more land to build on, and we all know what's happened to the price of land.

In a master bedroom down design, all the essential living areas are on one level, including sleeping, bathing, eating, and entertaining areas. The second level includes additional bedrooms for children and guests, and secondary work and entertainment spaces. If the home owners don't want to climb stairs, they don't have to.

In choosing designs for a master bedroom down house, you will generally discover that the best layouts have more living space on the ground level than on the second level. This can be accomplished by having part of the house be a one-story design, and part two-story. This also creates a more interesting exterior layout and "streetscape" for the house. The other way is to open up interior spaces to create "volume spaces" in the home. A two-story foyer or great room can open up the interior of a home and provide exciting, light-filled spaces.

The parent zone

Another advantage of the master bedroom down design is the separation it gives parents and children. When children are very small, parents often want their bedrooms nearby in case of emergencies. As the children grow and become teenagers, both the children and the parents want more privacy and peace and quiet in their lives. Parents don't want to have to deal with loud music and messy rooms. The children want more autonomy and independence. Putting the master bedroom down creates two separate zones, provides the separation they both need, and improves the quality of family life.

Indoor/outdoor living

The master bedroom down design also gives the master bedroom suite greater access to the outside. French doors and patios and decks directly off the master bedroom bring the outdoors inside and greatly expand the visual space.

In addition, the light pouring into the rooms makes them more pleasant and liveable. Psychological studies have shown that people tend to gravitate to those living spaces that provide light and access to nature. By bringing light into the master bedroom, you've created greater livability for the entire house, and increased perceived value. If they fall in love with the master bedroom, you have a better chance of selling the house.

Flexibility

If you're smart, you can design the same house as both a master bedroom up or a master bedroom down version. This gives your potential buyers a choice and can satisfy different buyers' needs. This way, you gain the advantages of building the same house more than once, while expanding your potential buyer base. The house shown is basically the same house, except for the master bedroom location.

Building and selling homes is about satisfying buyer needs and wants. With all the advantages of the master bedroom down to an aging buyer base, make sure that you offer your buyers the excitement and livability of this design option.

Make Room for the Three-Car Garage

As houses become larger and more elaborate, the need for additional garage space also increases. The two-car family is now the rule, rather than the exception, and as children grow older, families often have more than two vehicles. Boats, jet skis, snowmobiles, lawn tractors, work benches, etc., also increase the demand for garage storage. In some parts of the country, it's not unusual to find a three-car garage attached to a 1,200 square-foot house. And if that's what buyers want, that's what builders will provide.

Since the three-car garage is becoming a way of life, the real question is how can it be integrated into the design of the house in order to maximize curb appeal. Here are four ways to focus attention on the house rather than the garage.

The main body of the house should be more visually prominent than the garage. If the house is higher (two-story vs. one-story) and has more interesting visual elements (intersecting gables, columns, porches) it will draw the eye toward the entrance rather than the garage. If you move the garage further back from the street, it will also reduce its visual dominance.

Sideloading

If the lot is wide enough, you can sideload the garage (enter from the side rather than the street). This allows the garage to look like an integral part of the house itself, and makes the house look larger, increasing curb appeal. Since the large garage doors don't face the street, they are less intrusive.

Splitting

If you can't sideload the garage due to the width of the lot, try splitting the garage into a two-car section and a one-car section. Then set the one-car garage further back to minimize its visual impact. You can also minimize impact by having a separate garage-door opening for each bay and painting the doors to blend in with the siding.

Camouflage

Use landscaping and architectural elements to disguise the garage. Trees planted at the edge of the garage soften the silhouette of the house. Wing walls, hedging, and fencing can visually lengthen the house and draw the eye away from the garage. Tapering down the driveway and offsetting the drive can minimize the effect of a 20-foot-wide ribbon of paving which leads the eyes directly to the garage doors.

The three-car garage should be designed to contribute rather than detract from the overall impression of the home. Look for home plans that provide the garage space you need and present an integrated and attractive impression to the buyer. By combining function with curb appeal, you can provide more garage space in an attractive package.

Developing a Product Line

To maximize sales success, builders would do well to emulate the automobile manufacturers and create not just a product but a product line – a series of products that meets different needs yet works together to create a unified image. This is especially true when you're building homes next to each other in the same community. By creating a unified image, you enhance the visual consistency of the neighborhood while introducing a pleasing variety of compatible styles.

The other advantage to a product line is that it limits buyer choices. People want choices, but prefer a range of options to choose from rather than having to start from the ground up. Imagine how difficult it would be to buy a car if your salesman gave you a blank piece of paper and said, "Tell us what you want. We'll design it and build it for you, based on your desires." By limiting the buyers' choices but giving them lots of flexibility in terms of design, finishes, components, and styles, buyers have the best of both worlds. So does the builder – he knows what to expect. In creating a product line, here are some things to keep in mind:

Consistency and variety

These two concepts may seem to be contradictory, but they're not. Consistency in a product line is shown through similar roof lines, housing styles, and attention to detail. Variety comes from different exterior materials, colors, layouts, and massing. It's okay to mix architectural styles in the same neighborhood as long as they're compatible. A craftsman-style home can relate well to a colonial style, for example, but neither relate well to an ultra-modern style.

Different houses for different needs

When you create a community, you want to appeal to a broad base of needs, within certain socioeconomic limits. Families vary in size, composition, interests, and spatial needs. Families with small children may want an upstairs bedroom to be near the children. Families with teenagers may want a bedroom on the ground floor to give everyone some "space," and to create one-level living for the parents. Some families place a high value on entertaining, others on privacy and family activities. By creating a product line of compatible houses that satisfies different needs, you have a higher probability of closing the sale.

Design flexibility

To further boost your chances of closing the sale, each house should have as much design flexibility as possible. Bedrooms should be designed so they can also be used as home offices, play spaces, or libraries. Dining rooms should be flexible enough to be used as either formal entertainment spaces or first-floor studies. Point out that the "bonus space" created over the garage has many possible uses – extra bedrooms, family rooms, exercise areas, etc. The more flexibility you build in, the easier, more cost-effective it will be to modify the design for the buyer.

Buildability

Now that you have a product line, you can build the same basic home over and over again, while tailoring the plan to each buyer. Make sure the plan is cost-effective to build so buyers get the most value for their money. Look for simplified (but not boring) rooflines, buildable spans, and affordable materials. Wherever possible, standardize components such as windows, doors, fireplace details, etc.

Curb appeal

Buyers should fall in love with your homes at first sight. This means interesting massing, good use of materials and attention to exterior details. It also means attention to landscaping and how the houses are sited on the lot. In designing a product line, however, remember that the exterior look of the home is practically interchangeable. If the buyers want a colonial look, a craftsman style, a Victorian, or a cottage style, they can have these with nearly any interior they choose. In fact, we recommend developing at least two different elevations for each interior layout; this gives the buyer more options and creates variety in your subdivision.

If you don't have a consistent product line now, develop one to give yourself a competitive edge. If you have a product line, but it's getting worn around the edges, it's time to redesign it or develop a new one. Either way, you can increase your sales, stream-line your estimating and construction and increase your profits.

Indoor/Outdoor Living

The size and placement of rooms and the way rooms "feel" determine the livability of a home. An often-overlooked way to expand that feel and livability is by using the concept of "indoor/outdoor living." Too many builders design and construct a lovely home but don't take the time to site it properly on a lot to take advantage of views and light. Or they create a beautiful home in a beautiful setting, and then tack a tiny deck onto the back of the house. As a result, the home fails to take advantage of its setting, and fails to create the perceived value that would increase the saleable price. Ironically, on a square-foot basis, indoor/outdoor living is the least expensive way to increase the livability of the home.

In designing indoor/ outdoor living, consider these three major concepts: 1) transition areas, 2) expanding indoor rooms, and 3) creating outdoor rooms.

Transition areas

At every transition between the indoors and the outdoors, take special care to make that transition as pleasant as possible. Entranceways to a home should be covered and protected from the weather, through a porch or covered entry. This way you and your guests can be out of the snow or rain while you fumble for your keys or umbrella, or while they wait for someone to come to the door. In the back, an arbor or pergola can shade and soften the light that enters the home.

Expanding the indoors

Make indoor rooms feel much larger by opening them to the outdoors through windows and glass doors, and through placement of outdoor spaces. A living room or a bedroom that opens onto a spacious deck or patio seems much larger than one that is closed in on itself. In fact, it not only seems larger; it is larger since people will use those outdoor areas as living spaces in nice weather. A bedroom, for example, that opens onto a private garden adds color and warmth to the room year round. It provides visual interest as the weather shifts and the light changes during the day. This variety within uniformity provides a psychological comfort to the occupants and adds to their living pleasure.

The trick here is to use the Zen concept of limited perspective to create comfortable areas. A solid wall of glass, for example, often feels less comfortable than a series of divided windows that frame the vista and open to the outdoors and at the same time create a sense of enclosure and protection.

Creating outdoor rooms

For a space to be truly functional and comfortable, it has to be defined with well-marked boundaries and designed on a human scale. Rooms that are too large can be as uncomfortable as rooms that are too small. This is true whether those spaces are indoors or outdoors. Decks and patios create living areas that allow comfortable interpersonal interaction and facilitate human activity. Outdoor furniture, benches, barbecues, and sports areas such as badminton, volleyball, tetherball, pools, terraces – all these allow the family and guests to interact in a positive fashion. It doesn't take much to
define a space. A half wall or plantings around a patio does the job. You can use trees, hedges, and terraces to divide a large, uncomfortable space into a series of smaller, more intimate spaces that can be enjoyed by all.

When you compare the cost of creating a square foot of living space outdoors with the cost indoors, and you look at the added benefits in terms of enhanced enjoyment and livability, indoor/ outdoor living is a concept that should be integrated in the design of every new home.

Let There Be Light

In designing a new home, one of the most neglected, yet important aspects is the quality of natural light in each room. If you don't believe this, you should walk through a new home with a prospective buyer, and watch their eyes as they enter a cheerful, light-filled room. Their eyes widen in delight, and they get smiles on their faces. Then watch as they enter a dark, claustrophobic space. The smiles disappear.

People are often not even aware of this emotional reaction. They just know that deep down inside, they're rather be in the room with soft, even light. In every home, people gravitate to those spaces. They often become the central social space of the home, regardless of the room's original function. They avoid the darker spaces, unless they're forced to go there.

Many builders don't understand this. They feel that if they put a window in a room, and an overhead light in the ceiling, that should satisfy the light requirement. If they need more light, they use a bigger window (or more of them.) But this often fails to deal with the emotional aspects of the way light improves the quality of a home. Here are some basic rules for improving the quality of light in your homes:

1. Put light on two sides of every room

This basic insight comes from Christopher Alexander's book, *A Pattern Language*. When light enters a room from more than one direction, it softens and diffuses the light, reducing glare, and getting light to every corner of the room. Christopher Alexander feels that this is the single most important rule in creating livable, inviting rooms. It can be difficult to follow this rule for every room, but it's critically important for social spaces such as family and living rooms, and for master bedrooms.

Sometimes you can't put light on two sides due to the room layout or placement. But it's a good rule to follow when you can.

2. Place windows for light, not just for view

Sometimes a builder will avoid putting windows in the ends of houses, to avoid looking out directly at the neighbors. The other night I drove through a neighborhood of nice new single-family homes, and not a single home had windows in the ends, not even for the master bedroom. One solution is to put the windows higher up, where they add light, but not view. The secondary benefit is that this way you can add windows without making furniture arrangement difficult. This is a strategy that Frank Lloyd Wright used often in his houses. Whatever else he may have been, he was a master of the use of light.

3. Use artificial light to compensate for lack of natural light

In some home designs it's difficult to get light on two sides of every room. The solution here is to use artificial light to balance the light levels. For example, light sconces on the wall opposite the windows are an excellent solution.

4. Use diffuse light where possible

A light valance that reflects light off the ceiling may cost more than a central light fixture, but it creates a very even and dramatic lighting pattern. You can use this in special rooms, such as dining rooms and bedrooms that don't require high levels of task lighting. Of course, the best way to diffuse natural light is to filter it through the leaves of trees.

5. Use light as a selling point

If you're going to go to the trouble of integrating good lighting into your home design, make sure the potential client sees it and understands that this is a benefit. We use a silent salesman (a poster on the wall) that says:

> **Let there be light**
> The quality of light often determines how comfortable a room can be. That's why we pay special attention to make every room as spacious and light-filled as possible. We try to place windows so that light enters from two sides of the room. We use Andersen windows to avoid drafts and maximize energy efficiency. And we build in ambient and accent lighting so that even at night your rooms are filled with light and enjoyment.
>   Wouldn't you like a little light in your life?

By paying special attention to the use of light in your home, you can set yourself apart from the average builder. Putting more light in your homes can put more profit in your pocket.

Designing the Neighborhood

A neighborhood is different than a subdivision or a development. It's more than just a collection of houses and streets and sidewalks. It implies that there is system of social interaction that allows a collection of disparate, busy people to fuse together in a way that enriches their lives. This social interaction doesn't just happen by accident. It must be thought through by the developer so that it increases the value of the entire community. People are willing to pay for such intangible concepts as "quality of life." If you aren't willing to sell those intangibles through neighborhood design, you're simply throwing away potential profit.

Elements of a neighborhood

To turn a subdivision into a neighborhood, the developer has to think about and integrate community identity, product mix, community space, community access, and circulation.

Community identity

Just giving your community a name and putting up an entrance sign doesn't create community identity. What you need is a cultural and historical reality – even if you have to make it up. Every piece of land has a history attached to it ... previous owners, uses, events. Use these as part of your marketing and design to create instant "roots" for your new community.

Product mix

Plan your community to meet a wide range of housing needs and demographics. However, those needs need to be consistent and compatible. It's perfectly okay (exciting, in fact) to mix upscale townhomes and single family homes in the same neighborhood. It's okay to mix age-groups (young families and empty nesters). You can include homes of different size ranges, and targeted to different needs (young professionals and empty-nesters). What you have to be careful of, however, is to make those products compatible economically. If you're targeting high-end buyers, all products should be high end. If you're targeting midpoint, don't mix high-end townhomes and midpoint single families.

The product mix should also be compatible stylistically. They should incorporate compatible exterior styles (classic and craftsman, for example). They should use similar levels of detail. However, stylistic compatibility does not mean boring repetition. You want variety of design and styles to create a more vibrant streetscape. The days of cookie-cutter urban sprawl are on their way out.

Community space

If you want people to meet and fuse socially, you have to provide an environment in which that can happen. In a larger community that can mean a community park or recreation center. In a smaller community, it can mean providing places for recreation and just sitting and conversation. A covered public patio can provide a focal point and a place for activities.

Community access

Every new community must relate to the larger community in which it is found. Nearby shopping, schools, employment centers, recreation and cultural centers are all important and must be integrated into your community planning. Is there an easy way to get to these areas? Can children access them without being chauffeured by too-busy parents?

Circulation

Our current subdivision design has long been dominated by the automobile. Front-loaded garages, wide streets, lack of sidewalks create a situation where you can only get to where you want to go by getting into the automobile and driving. When we were kids you could go nearly every-where on your bike. Today, traffic make that dangerous and undesirable.

In planning your community, make what small changes you can to make it a place that is human-scale and people friendly. Rear- or side-loaded garages improve the aesthetics and create more of a neighborhood "feel." Bike paths and sidewalks allow people to get outside and walk (which is also good exercise). Create a community focal point to give them someplace to go. Increase community density (if zoning allows) to reduce street frontage required.

Since every home is located in a community, good community design increases the perceived value of every home you sell.

5
It's the Profits, Stupid

P rofit is the lubricant that makes the machinery of business run smoothly. It provides a cash cushion that allows you to weather the inevitable ups and downs of the building business. It can provide operating capital to fuel growth and deal with emergencies. And it provides the psychological incentive to improve your productivity and competitiveness. Without sufficient profit, the well eventually runs dry, and the company breaks down and dies.

Profits are the direct result of excellence

The interesting thing about profits is that they are the direct result of doing things right. If you focus exclusively on making money, you can lose sight of all the factors that go into profit: good products, good service, good marketing, and good management. Without these, there is no profit. If you're doing all these things right, increased profit is nearly automatic.

What's your Profit IQ?

Profit IQ is the intelligence with which you pursue and generate profit. A low IQ means you lose a little on each job, and try to make up for it in volume. A high IQ means that the profit impact is the primary consideration of every decision.

Keeping your eye on the profits is like keeping your eye on the ball – it's the only way to win.

> **"The happiest time in any man's life is when he is in red-hot pursuit of a dollar, with a reasonable prospect of overtaking it."**
>
> — Josh Billings

123

4 Ways to Build Profits

Everyone who builds houses expects to make a profit. Yet I talk to thousands of builders across the country, and many of them complain that their profits are dwindling, and they don't know what to do about it. So let's go back to basics. There are four basic ways to increase your profits: Increase your prices, lower your costs, lower your overhead, or increase your sales volume. That's it. If you can't do one or more of these things, you can't increase your profits.

Increase your prices

Many builders tell me that they're in a highly competitive market, and that they can't raise their prices. But the price you can charge is a function of the value you provide. Perceived value is a function of design, location, materials, and quality of construction. These must be properly balanced to get the maximum perceived value for the minimum cost.

Lower your costs

The fastest way to lower your production costs is to simplify construction. At the beginning of every new job, I go through the plans carefully to see where the design can be improved and simplified.

The other major area of cost reduction is in component selection. However, be very careful here. Using cheap products can lower the perceived value of the entire home. But you *can* eliminate outrageously expensive components where it doesn't matter. For example, you can often substitute marble tile for sheet marble or granite. It's much less expensive. You can also lower your labor costs by using more efficient subs. A sub that comes in a few dollars cheaper on an estimate doesn't save you any money if he takes a week longer to complete the job, or delays the work of other subcontractors.

Lower your overhead

Overhead is the money you spend to stay in business. It includes salary for office staff, rent, telephone, office supplies, computers, etc. For most small volume and custom builders, the big jumps in overhead occur

It's the Profits, Stupid

when an extra person is hired. The trick is to increase sales volume and profit while keeping overhead constant. This effectively decreases overhead as a percentage of total sales. There is a point of diminishing returns as personnel are stretched to the limits of their capacity. That's the time to add the extra person in order to jump up to the next level of capability.

One way to lower your overhead is to increase office efficiency. Using a computer to perform word processing, estimating, scheduling, and accounting functions can actually save money by enabling you to get more done in less time, and with less people. But don't get carried overboard. Simpler systems are usually better than complex ones.

Increase your sales volume

After you have pricing, costs, and overhead under control, then think about ways to increase your sales volume. Increasing your sales volume only increases your profits if you can maintain (or increase) your present profit margins. I've seen builders who lowered prices to increase sales and discovered they were building twice as many houses, yet making less money. That makes no sense to me. Why work twice as hard, when you can work a little smarter, and still come out ahead?

The best way to increase your profits is to look at all four of these ways simultaneously. By increasing your value (and raising your prices), lowering your costs, lowering your overhead, and increasing your sales volume, you may find that you can increase your total profits. Building houses is a lot more fun when you make a profit doing it.

Growing Your Business

Many builders reach a point in their business when they begin to question their ability to move forward and whether the things that made them successful will continue to work. Others plunge ahead and discover later that increased growth does not necessarily lead to increased profits or even financial success. Instead, increased growth can lead to increased overhead, production inefficiency, personnel problems and additional commuting and logistical support.

If you find yourself at this stage, it is usually better to consolidate for a year or two and concentrate on increasing profitability through better management, streamlined expenses and increased efficiency. You may also want to play with your pricing and increase your margins. Here are some steps to take to help you grow successfully:

Shore up the staffing
As you grow, so must your staffing, especially at the field supervision level. You may need to find new subs or rely more on existing subs. In all this, however, don't neglect your existing staff. Morale can suffer if the work load increases dramatically or if chaos overwhelms your systems. When you hire for growth, try to hire from the bottom so that new personnel support the existing staff and don't threaten their sense of security.

Look at your margins
Margins vary across the country, but your minimum net profit should be somewhere between 5 and 7 %. Overhead is more difficult to benchmark because builders use different methods to account for items like the owner's salary. As the owner, you can increase overhead and lower net profits by taking out a large salary and generous benefits. Or you can draw a small salary and slim benefits to build a larger net profit, which might then be reduced by a substantial bonus. (More conservative builders leave the profits in the company and use them to buy more land and create additional opportunities.)

While it's difficult to suggest a specific overhead percentage, many custom builders successfully run their companies with a ratio of approximately one employee per $700,000 to $1.2 million in gross sales revenues.

Consider a consultant

If you find yourself growing beyond your comfort level, it might be time to hire someone who can look at your current situation and discuss future opportunities and goals. A good consultant helps you focus on what you need to do and helps you understand how to do it. Good consultants don't just impose their vision on your company.

Growing your business successfully requires capital, good people, and especially smart management. If you're going to grow, do it in a way that you manage the growth, rather than letting the growth manage you.

MAP Out Your Success

To get somewhere, you need to know where you're going. Imagine you're driving from Chicago to a city on the west coast. You aren't really sure of your destination. You don't have a map, and you haven't decided what the best routes are between these two cities. It's possible to get from one city to the other without a map. But you won't get there as fast, and you'll probably get lost several times along the way.

Management Action Plans are the MAPs for your company. They help you decide where you're going, and how to get there. The key word is *action*. Any plan that does not lead to action is a waste of time. Most business plans suffer from the following fatal flaws:

Too comprehensive. They try to deal with every aspect of a company's future, and are therefore difficult to create and to understand. They tend to be treated as a sacred cow – something we pay lip service to but ignore in everyday life.

Too difficult to implement. By anticipating every major contingency, they become unwieldy blueprints for imposing edifices. Because they can't be implemented step-by-step, they aren't implemented at all.

Too inflexible. They try to freeze the future so that unpredictable things don't happen. Unfortunately, the world isn't like that. A management *action* plan is a living, evolving document that provides concrete guidance for implementing the growth of your company. As the market changes and as your company changes, the plan changes, too. It can become the driving force that channels growth and activity into profitable areas.

Three reasons you need a MAP

1. A MAP is the blueprint for the construction of your business. Just as you use a blueprint to build a house, you use a business plan to tell you how to build a business. Unlike a blueprint, it's okay to make changes as you go along and discover new ideas and directions.

128   **It's the Profits, Stupid**

2. A MAP is a marvelous exercise in defining your business and exploring options and opportunities. Even if it had no other function, the plan would justify your effort just on this one purpose alone.

3. A MAP provides lenders, investors, and customers insights into who you are and where you are going. It tells them that they have a better chance of seeing a positive return on their investment.

Marketing, management, and money

There are three major areas you have to map out as part of your business plan – marketing, management, and money. The Marketing MAP tells you how to effectively create customers. You can't build houses if no one buys them. It tells who your target market is, what products you intend to provide them, how you intend to reach them, and how you position your company against the competition.

The Management MAP focuses on the people, systems, organization, and functions that help you organize for success. Without clear-cut areas of responsibility, people will not work together to form an efficient team.

The Money MAP tells you what resources you need for capital formation and for maintaining the day-to-day operations. It consists of the following elements: revenue projections (pro forma), cash flow analysis, overhead analysis, capital requirements, and a loan repayment plan. Your Money MAP should be reasonable, rather than overly optimistic. Don't use unrealistic sales expectations to justify high overhead expenditures or high capital investment. In fact, don't even do a Money MAP until you've done your Marketing and Management MAPs.

By writing a Management Action Plan, you begin thinking about the steps you need to take to ensure the success of your business and prepare to travel down the road to your destination.

Shopping the Competition

To keep ahead, you have to know who your competitors are and what they are doing

Marketing competition is a form of warfare. And the first rule of warfare is "know your enemy." You should make a consistent effort to know what your competition is offering, and what you can do to gain a competitive advantage.

Many builders today are like the American car companies in the 1970s and 1980's. They lost their competitive edge and keep offering the same old product, year after year. By the time the American car companies woke up, the Japanese had stolen a significant market share away from them by building a better product and responding to consumer needs. Don't let it happen to you.

In order to keep your competitive edge, you need to visit your competition's homes or sales offices, pick up, copies of their sales literature, and carefully compare their products and way of doing business with your own. When you shop the competition, you're basically looking for the following information:

Who is my competition?

What are my competitors doing right (that I could adapt to my own business)?

What are they doing wrong (that I can take advantage of)?

What marketing methods are they using to reach those consumers?

Who is my competition?

Not every builder out there is your competitor. The housing market is extremely segmented, and you can learn a lot from how other builders try to reach that market, whether they are direct competitors or not.

One of the best methods of comparison shopping is to go to a different geographic market, and study the competition there.

What are they doing right?

If your competitors were doing everything wrong, they wouldn't be your competitors for long. You can learn a lot from your competition –

new product ideas, new procedures, new marketing techniques. If it's a good idea, adapt it to your own way of building. However, don't slavishly copy your competition. You want to be better than they are, not carbon copies. Take the good ideas and make them better.

What are they doing wrong?

If your competition is weak in some area (outdated designs, cumbersome procedures, poor customer service), then you need to exploit that weakness by emphasizing your strengths in your marketing message. The trick here is to be positive, not negative. When you criticize your competitor directly, you do two things wrong. First, you create awareness and recognition for your competition. Secondly, you create a negative atmosphere, and it's hard for potential buyers to feel positive about you in a negative environment.

What are their marketing methods?

If you have a better product, but your competition has better marketing, you will lose a lot of potential buyers who never even get the chance to buy your product. But be very careful not to copy their marketing message. A "me-too" campaign almost never works. You need to know what their marketing message is, however, in order to create a different message for yourself. Just be certain that the quality of your materials and the strength of your message compare favorably.

By shopping your competition on a regular basis, you can avoid the complacency that leads to loss of market share, you can quickly adapt to changes in the marketplace, and you can keep your eyes and ears open to new opportunities for cooperation. Make it a regular part of your business strategy.

10 Ways Builders Mess Up Their Business

There's never a lack of opportunity for builders to mess up their business and kill their profits. Here are ten of the most common.

1. **Poor pricing decisions.** One of the hardest things for builders to do is get their price right. Price too high and the product sits. Price too low and you lose profit or go broke. Solution: price for profit, and adjust for the market. Most builders use cost-based pricing. They figure what it costs to build and then tack on a percentage. The second type of pricing is value-based. This is what the market will pay. Value-based pricing is the one that ultimately prevails in the market. If the builder's cost-based pricing is higher than the market-based pricing, the builder will have to find a way to reduce his costs (or accept a lower profit).

2. **Building a ho-hum house.** One reason builders can't get a better price for their houses is that there's nothing special about them. They're like all the other houses, cluttering the market and competing on price alone. To go from a ho-hum house to a hot house is often a matter of simple redesign.

3. **Building in the wrong location.** (Bad neighborhood, bad lot). Builders think that if they build a nice house on a bad lot people will buy it anyway. A good house doesn't compensate for a bad lot. A bad lot makes a good house bad.

4. **Overbuilding for the market.** To set themselves apart from the competition, some builders think they have to build the fanciest (and costliest) house around. It's always better to be the least expensive house in a good neighborhood than the most expensive house in a so-so neighborhood. If you overbuild, you won't get your money back.

5. **Unrealistic expectations.** We do such a good job of selling clients on what a great builder we are that they expect perfection. When things

It's the Profits, Stupid

go wrong (and they always do), they're disappointed. It doesn't have to be that way. If your clients understand that there is no such thing as a "perfect" house, they'll be happier (and so will you).

6. Poor sub supervision. Much of the work of building a home is done by subcontractors, but the builder is responsible for seeing that the work is done on time, and done right. Slipping schedules and poor quality control are indications that the builder isn't doing his job.

7. Sloppy cost control. Some builders don't know if they've made money until the house is complete. Then they discover change orders that should have been submitted and avoidable cost overruns. Look at every job every month to see that costs are under control.

8. Inaccurate estimating. Sometimes builders really want to get a job. Without realizing it, they underestimate to get the costs where they want them. If you want to lower your prices to get a job, that's your business. But don't lie to yourself that you're making more profit than you really are.

9. Selling features, not benefits. Builders are so fixated on building that they often neglect to tell consumers what the product will do for them. People don't care about features.

10. Makeshift marketing. If you don't have a strong marketing message or good marketing materials, you may be in trouble. Good marketing creates awareness and value perception.

There are a lot of ways that builders can mess up their business. How many of them are you guilty of?

Advise and Consent

Local experts can give your company a fresh outlook

One of the biggest problems successful builders face is that they become stuck in a rut. They continue doing things that have worked well for them in the past, but the market changes and they no longer work. Then they wonder what went wrong.

To avoid this kind of problem, major corporations create an advisory board composed of people outside the company and the industry. This board provides a fresh outlook on the problems and directions of the corporation.

While most small- to medium-sized builders may not want to go to all the trouble of creating a formal board of directors, they can reap the same benefits by forming an informal board of advisors.

The board should meet several times a year to discuss strategic direction. It shouldn't get involved in the day-to-day operations of the company, but should look at the *big picture* – how competitive you are, how your product compares with market needs, if there are unmet market opportunities your company could fill, and how resources are allocated to improve productivity and profitability.

The job of the informal board is to give you advice and act as a sounding board for any new directions you're considering. The board can provide a fresh perspective on problems you're facing and help to avoid major mistakes. In the immortal words of Woody Allen, "Two heads are better than one, unless they're on the same body."

So who should be on this informal board of advisors? Start with people who understand the industry and the market. Do you have a real estate agent you trust? An architect or designer with whom you like to work? A past customer who's particularly savvy about consumer needs? Perhaps an expert of management at the local college? All of these people can provide an outsider viewpoint and generate new ideas for your company. Remember that each of them may have a particular bias, and that the best ideas come about from the interplay of differing viewpoints. Make sure that you have both men and women on your board; after all, that's who you're selling to. And you should offer to pay them a small honorarium as compensation for their time and energy.

Make sure that the meetings are fun. Meet in pleasant surroundings, and treat your "advisors" like VIPs. Provide an agenda of things you want to discuss in advance, and leave enough flexibility in the agenda so you have time to explore in unanticipated directions. Afterwards, do some fun activity together.

It takes a little work and thought on your part to create this outside advisory board, but it can make you money in the long run by steering your business in new and profitable directions.

6
People Power

There's an old saying that many builders believe: "If you want something done right, do it yourself." Unfortunately, following that adage is a recipe for disaster in business. Unless you're running a hot dog vending stand, you really can't make it on your own in today's world. No matter how smart you are, and no matter how hard you work, you can accomplish more and have greater success by relying on the hard work and intelligence of others.

The problem we face, however, is how to get other people to do things the way we would want them done, without our having to constantly look over their shoulder and tell them what to do every step of the way.

That's what people power is all about. Finding, hiring, motivating, and keeping first-rate people, who will think and act independently and make profits for you and themselves. It means evaluating your management style and compensating for your weaknesses. It means finding good professional collaborators, and even working closely with competitors in order to better satisfy the needs and wants of your customers.

"Nothing so needs reforming
as other people's habits."
— Mark Twain

Finding and Hiring Good People

Among the most common questions I receive are those concerning personnel-whom to hire, how to hire, how to provide long-term motivation, and how to fire people when they don't perform. Here are some guidelines to help builders tackle these topics:

1. Look for what's important

We call this putting "A before E." People are often hired based on their experience and education. But attitude and aptitude are much more important. What you're looking for is someone who's willing to work and succeed and is able to learn and grow. When those two traits are present, you can provide both the education and the experience, especially when you staff from the bottom up (see step 2). It's much easier to mold and shape someone who is able and willing to learn than try to change or correct someone who already has set ideas and preconceived notions.

2. Hire from the bottom

Wherever possible, hire good people at the lowest levels of your organization. For example, if your superintendent is overworked, think about hiring an assistant superintendent instead of a second super. Why? Not just because the cost of an assistant employee is less than that of an experienced super, but also for these reasons:

■ The existing employee feels important (the new person is someone to help him) rather than threatened (not someone with whom to compete).

■ You can mold the new employee the way you want. He or she hasn't picked up a set of ingrained habits that may conflict with the way you want to do things.

■ You provide an upward migration path. By hiring from the bottom, you enable people to look forward to the possibility of promotion.

3. Share the wealth

Nothing motivates employees like a chance to participate in corporate success. In today's competitive marketplace, a form of profit sharing is a must if you wish to ensure loyalty and keep outstanding people. A key point to remember is that while other fringe benefits cost you money whether or not you make a profit, this one only costs money when you make money. Writing a large profit-sharing payment to your employees is not an expense – it's a celebration.

4. Follow your instincts

The best time to fire someone is when you think of it the first time. When I first heard this, I questioned it, yet it contains an element of truth. When you reach a point where you actually consider firing someone, it's probably the time to do so. How many of us hold on much too long, trying to be fair, waiting for an employee to change his or her bad habits?

Unfortunately, people rarely change. If they keep repeating the same mistakes, the time to fire them is now, not six months from now, after they've made a lot more mistakes.

Hiring good people who want to work hard, finding ways to motivate them, and quickly letting go of those who don't measure up will go a long way toward making your organization stronger and better.

Motivating and Retaining Good People

No matter how smart you are, and no matter how hard you work, you ultimately have to rely on other people to increase your productivity. People power is the art of getting the greatest productivity and profitability from your employees and the people who work with you.

A recent survey of managers and employees across the country provides an interesting insight into the changing work environment. Employees were asked to rank ten factors that affect job satisfaction in order of importance to them. Managers were asked to rank the same factors. The managers responded as you might expect: They rated good wages as the most important criteria, followed by job security. But the employees responses were surprising. The most important criteria was "work that keeps you interested." The second most important criteria was "appreciation of work done." Good wages was rated eighth out of ten factors.

There are seven elements to People Power and they all start with the letter P. They are: **P**raise, **P**ay, **P**leasant environment, **P**erks and privileges, **P**roductivity tools and education, **P**romotion, and **P**rofit sharing.

Praise

It's amazing how hard people will work for a little recognition. It costs you nothing but makes everyone feel better. If it's hard for you to tell people when they're doing a good job, you need to change your attitude. Don't rely on formalized awards – people need continual, daily reinforcement.

Pay them what they're worth

How do you determine how much people are worth? One theory is the marketplace value: An employee is worth what someone else is willing to pay them. To secure employee loyalty, you may have to pay them a little bit more. The other theory is contribution value: They are worth a percentage of the contribution their efforts make to the overall company profits. This is sometimes hard to measure, since many critical factors are hard to quantify.

How do you measure the contribution of an architectural designer, for example? Pay may not be the most important incentive for employees, but it can be a powerful *dis*incentive, if they perceive that their contribution isn't recognized or valued. They shouldn't feel so undervalued that they have to find a new job just to be fairly compensated. If you had to replace them, what would it cost you?

Top-rated people always cost more than second-rate people. Second-rate people are always willing to work for less, but their productivity and contribution to profits is also much less. In the end, they cost a lot more. If you want to compete in today's market, you can't afford second-rate employees.

Pleasant work environment

Your offices don't have to be luxurious, but they should be clean, attractive, and well-lit. The emotional atmosphere should be supportive and professional. If your people are playing office politics and assigning blame rather than taking responsibility, you have a problem. People take their cues from the boss. If you encourage people to admit mistakes and then correct them, you'll create a more pleasant working atmosphere.

Perks and privileges

With increased responsibility there should also be an increase in autonomy. Corporate credit cards for business related expenses, corporate retreats, special vacation packages, all say that an employee is trusted and valued. However, perks should be earned, rather than simply attached to a job level. If all the privileges go to the people at the top, it becomes a disincentive to the people below.

Productivity tools and education

To keep your people sharp, you have to constantly reeducate them to the changing needs of the market. People get stale and set in their ways, and need a jolt to their way of thinking every once in a while. In addition, technology is changing so fast that much of what you knew two years ago is now obsolete. Computers are changing the way we do business. If your people use computers, upgrade the equipment regularly (every two years or so), and make sure they know how to use the latest software. Don't be like the guy who hired Einstein, and then made him fill out a requisition for chalk.

Promotion opportunities

As people demonstrate they can handle responsibility, you should give them more and more. Be careful, however, that you don't promote them out of the work they enjoy. If they're a hands-on, outdoors type of person, and you promote them to a desk job, they may appreciate the vote of confidence, but hate what they do all day.

We have a tendency to think that management positions should be more highly paid than hands-on work. However, the real issue is contribution to profits. If someone out in the field is making a major contribution to profits then they should compensated accordingly, regardless of hierarchial level.

Wherever you can, hire from the bottom, and promote from within. Not only do you save money, but you have less problems with "culture shock." A new person brought in at a low level adopts your corporate culture. When you bring someone in at the top, they often bring with them their own way of doing things, which may, or may not be compatible with your own. Of course, sometimes you want a change in corporate culture, and hiring someone with a different approach is one way to accomplish this.

The main reason for promoting from within, however, is that it rewards your people for their work and loyalty, and tells the entire company that there are future opportunities for them based on their efforts.

Profit sharing

Ultimately you want the people that work with you to always think in terms of profits. When they do that, they automatically look for ways to reduce expenses, and increase sales and productivity. The best way to teach them to think that way is to give them a share of the profits.

If you follow the seven P's of People Power, you'll find that your company will attract a higher quality of personnel, and that your present personnel will be more highly motivated, productive, and happy. That leads to greater profits for you, and for them.

Collaborating for Success

The world of 1996 is a different place than it was 10 or 20 or 30 years ago. The key today is to find those strategies that enable a builder to be successful in the new, more complicated, more technical environment.

In the past many builders were basically crew chiefs and master carpenters. They understood construction quite well and built large numbers of basic homes. As the market evolved and became more complex, builders had to learn management and financial skills. They became number crunchers as well as nail pounders. As builders became larger, they had to increase their staffing in order to ensure availability of design skills, computer skills and marketing skills. Today, the builder is more often a conductor of the orchestra, coordinating many disparate skills and abilities in order to create an exciting, profitable home.

Many small builders, however, lack the financial resources and cash flow necessary to have on-staff all the expertise they need. They can't play the violin and direct the orchestra at the same time. So how can the smaller builder compete with the large builders with their in-house expertise? The answer is simple: through Collaboration. The Law of Collaboration says to surround yourself with first-rate people and use their expertise to supplement your own. It doesn't say that those people have to be employees.

There are two ways to collaborate. One is by hiring outside experts on an as-needed basis. The other is by finding experts with whom you share a mutual interest. One area of collaboration is architectural design. A well-designed house often costs less to build than one poorly designed and it sells faster and at a higher price. But many designers don't really understand construction and charge high fees for custom work. If you find one who thinks like a builder, steer clients to those people. Or, you can offer their services as part of a total package. In return, they can steer clients to you. No money changes hands and yet everyone wins.

Another area of collaboration is marketing. If you can find a small one-man marketing firm that does writing as well as design, that's the best solution. If not, get good local design help and find someone who understands the marketing message.

It's difficult to find good management collaborators. Most of the so-called management experts really don't understand the very different world of the small builder. Find a good bookkeeper or accountant to help you run the financial side of your company and learn as much as you can about managing a small building business.

When you hire an outside expert, try to get the most bang for the buck. *Don't* use them to duplicate things that you can do. Let them develop ideas that you can implement. *Don't* tell them how to write or design. If you have a problem, tell them what it is and let them fix it. *Do treat* them like a valued partner. Call them when you have a question in their area of expertise. Listen to their advice, but don't follow it slavishly. Remember, you're the builder. You're the one who has to live with the decision.

If you learn to be an effective collaborator you can multiply your effectiveness by having experts at your fingertips without paying exorbitant overhead. It's the best of both worlds. You can effectively compete with your larger competitors by being leaner and smarter than they are.

Complementary Competition

Builders often view other builders as direct competition and see little reason to work with them. They think that every customer the other builder gets is a customer that they lose. Occasionally this is true when two equally strong builders have a similar product for a similar customer base in similar neighborhoods.

However, builders usually are not competing head-to-head. They have different customer profiles or build different styles of housing. Because each builder has a small portion of the total market, there are opportunities to cooperate with each other to expand their total market. Just as competing car dealers often locate next to each other to create a critical mass of customers, builders can learn to cooperate with each other to reinforce their market strengths.

Collaborating is the art of working with other people in order to accomplish more than you could on your own. There are many forms and levels of collaboration – and the higher the level, the more productive you can be. Collaboration allows you to minimize your weaknesses by working with people strong in those areas. Here are five reasons to collaborate with other builders:

Common agendas
You both are in the same business. You talk the same language. You understand how the other person thinks. Therefore, you can collaborate more easily.

Pool resources
For example, two builders working together could develop a tract of land that's too big for them to tackle individually.

Reduce indirect costs
Builders can share resources such as design, office management or consulting services to keep overhead under control and purchase services they could not otherwise afford.

Create a critical mass

Several builders working together in one location can take advantage of each other's advertising and marketing presence to draw more buyers.

Fill out product lines

Builders with complementary products like townhomes or single-family detached homes can meet a wider range of buyer needs by collaborating, rather than by trying to be all things to all people individually.

Often, a builder's best collaborators are fellow builders who may, or may not, compete directly. By working with them in a productive way, rather than fighting them or going alone, you both become better builders, better serve your customers, and become more profitable.

Motivating Subcontractors

Home building today is a team effort, with many independent subcontractors working together and providing their specialized skills. The builder or contractor acts as the quarterback of the team to motivate, direct and maintain quality control. Behavioral psychology says that there are only two ways to change behavior: reward and punishment.

In the long run, rewards are more successful, because they can be used to promote positive behaviors, while punishments can only be used to eliminate negative behaviors. In a competitive environment, motivating subcontractors isn't always easy. It requires a sense of fairness and reciprocity. In exchange for your subs' loyalty and support, you repay that loyalty by providing repeat business, referrals and prompt payment and by having reasonable quality expectations. If you are overly demanding, impossible to work for and slow to pay, they will transfer their loyalty to someone else. You won't get their best work or their highest scheduling priority.

Just as you may not always want the lowest bid sub on the job, you don't want the highest bid either. You need to keep your subs competitive in order to keep your own prices competitive. "The art of leadership," Napoleon Bonaparte said, "is to keep men from becoming stale."

When our subs become a bit complacent or less competitive with their prices, we usually sit down with them and have a conversation that goes like this: "Joe, I looked at your plumbing prices on the Baker job, and I think they're a little out of line. You've always done good work and you're one of my favorite contractors. I don't want to give this work to someone else. But unless we can come to some understanding about these prices, I'm going to have to give your competitor Pete a shot at one of our houses."

Here are five ways to motivate subcontractors:

Find what motivates them

Some people are highly sensitive to praise, others to financial rewards. Find out what makes them tick and use that to reward positive behavior.

Give continuous feedback

None of us likes to find out we've been doing things wrong for a while. When you see a problem, address it then. When you see something you like, say so then. Don't wait or the opportunity for positive reinforcement may be lost.

Use nonfinancial rewards liberally

You may be limited in how much you can reward your subs financially, but there are no limits on nonfinancial rewards. The most common (and under used) is praise, but special mementoes, awards and mention in corporate publications are also effective motivators at a minimal cost.

Be consistent

You can't praise someone one minute and later criticize him or her for the same behavior. Inconsistency is the fastest way to drive the people around you crazy (literally). Even consistent negative behavior is better than inconsistent behavior. At least your subs know what to expect.

Be fair

The fastest way to destroy morale is to play favorites. If a sub is rewarded based on any factor other than performance, the message quickly gets out and performance declines across the board.

Most builders use subcontractors extensively. Finding good reliable subs, retaining their loyalty, and motivating their performance can make your life easier, and contribute greatly to your success and profits.

7
Now What?

The problem with any book that provides information is "What do you do with the information once you have it?" After all, you didn't read this just for amusement (although we hope that it did give you a laugh from time to time). Turning insight into action is the hardest aspect of running a business.

That's why we added this section – to give you a way to begin thinking about applying these insights to your own business, diagnose your problems, and continue the process of learning, growing, changing, and improving. We've included essays on diversification (why you should and shouldn't) and exit strategies (what you should do when you're tired of building houses).

Building with an attitude does make the job more fun and profitable. But the ultimate determining factor of success is you: your attitude, your knowledge and information. Learning is a never-ending process. And just when you think you know it all is the time when everything changes and everything you thought you knew is wrong.

We are in one of those time periods when everything is changing. Customers are changing, our competitors are changing, and the way we do business will also change. So it's time for an attitude change also – one oriented towards more fun and profits.

"An ounce of action is worth a ton of theory."

— Friedrich Engels

Getting Things Done

Success in life is based not upon wealth and fame, but on our accomplishments. Getting things done requires effort and planning, a bias to action, and follow-through. Here are some general guidelines for getting things done.

Results, not effort

It's the results that counts, not the effort you put into it. Effort is important, and a certain amount of effort is required to get results, but the general rule of thumb is that 80% of your results will come from 20% of your efforts. The problem is figuring out where to put that 20% of effort.

Do the right things, rather than do things right

Peter Drucker points out that there are really two ways to improve your use of time. One is by spending your time *doing the right things* (effectiveness). The other is by *doing things right* (efficiency). But no matter how efficient you are, if you're doing the wrong things, you're getting nowhere. Drucker suggests spending 80% of your effort on *doing the right things*, and only 20% on *doing things right*.

Unfortunately, we spend a lot of time and energy trying to improve our efficiency, when the most efficient way to do something may be to not do it at all. Saying no to ineffective demands on our time frees us to spend that time more productively.

Direction, not speed

Think of effectiveness as direction and efficiency as speed. If we are moving in the right direction, however slowly, we are still getting closer to our destination. If we're traveling 90 miles an hour, we may be very efficient, but if we're going in the wrong direction, we'll never get there. In fact, we only get farther away.

People have a tendency to increase their speed once they lose their direction. It's as if all that hustle and bustle will somehow make up for the fact that what they're doing isn't that important.

Don't wait for the perfect plan

Just as you don't want to start driving before you know where you're going, you don't want to spend all your time deciding where to go, and no time getting there. (This is known as paralysis by analysis.) The thing about directions is that they can be corrected. If you have a map and make a wrong turn, you can quickly turn around and correct your course. This action, reaction, correction process is sometimes called muddling through, and is often the only way to go when you aren't quite sure where you're going. Perfection is the enemy of action. If you wait until your plan is perfect to implement it, you may never get the chance.

The big picture, vs. day-to-day

We sometimes get so caught up in the day-to-day operations of running a business that we forget to plan ahead for six months from now, a year from now. The time to think about next year is *now*, when you can do something about it. Get the big picture first, then fill in the details about how to accomplish that picture.

Success is not the absence of failure

One of the biggest barriers to getting things done is fear of failure. But if you put off doing the things that need to be done, you practically guarantee failure. One of Netscape's business maxims is "Fail quickly to succeed sooner." So don't be afraid to make mistakes. They're rarely fatal. Just correct them quickly and go on to other things.

The biggest problem in improving your business isn't deciding what to do – it's implementing the plan. The problem isn't solved until the plan is implemented. Make implementation planning part of every plan you do.

Why Diversify?

Whenever builders ask me a question about diversification I begin to get worried. Is another recession coming along? Is it time to get out of building for a while? What's the matter with the business they're in now? Is it too competitive?

There is no simple answer to the question of whether or not you should diversify. It all depends on who you are, and why you want to diversify. If you are successful at what you are doing, but feel you've saturated your market, then maybe diversification is a good thing. But if you're unsuccessful at homebuilding, there's no guarantee that you won't also be unsuccessful at light commercial construction, remodeling, etc. The grass only seems greener from the other side. When you get over there, you may find that it's a lovely green shade of crabgrass.

Some builders seem to want to diversify as a means of spreading risk. It's the old adage of "Don't keep all your eggs in one basket." And sometimes that's a smart idea. But sometimes it's also a smart idea to do as Mark Twain suggested: "Put all your eggs in one basket. And then *watch* that basket." You need to distinguish between diversifying your investments (nearly *always* a good idea) and diversifying your business (*sometimes* a good idea.) Your business provides a ongoing source of revenue from operations. Investments are what you do with the profits from the business. Builders historically keep putting all their profits back into the main business. The danger of that is that when a downcycle occurs, everything is at risk. By diversifying investment into other areas, you minimize the risk that a downturn in one area will be economically fatal.

In evaluating any diversification opportunities, ask yourself those two questions:

1. Does the diversification use skills and knowledge similar to the first business?

2. Is the new business counter cyclical with the old business? If the answer to either question is "No," think long and hard before diversifying.

There are four major diversification options for builders: vertical, horizontal, geographic, and other businesses.

Vertical diversification

Vertical diversification is where you look at the entire process of providing housing to consumers, and try to bring it all in-house. These include: land development, real estate, mortgage financing, and insurance.

Vertical integration usually occurs when the builder gets larger and volume justifies other operations. There are several problems with vertical integration. The first is that the builder may lack the specific expertise in these related fields, and by taking them in-house, may cut himself off from opportunities to collaborate with outside experts in those fields. You want those people working *with* you, not competing with you. The second major problem is that it really doesn't reduce your risk very much. These vertical markets are not counter cyclical. When the economy turns down in one area, it generally turns down in all the housing related areas. In fact, you may be increasing your risk by having all your businesses turn down at the same time.

There are a few advantages of vertical diversification. If it works, you "feed" several times off the same client – for land sales, real estate commissions, as well as home purchase. In addition, you control the buyer at major points in the purchase process, and have less risk of losing the buyer due to lender or agency problems.

A major builder in our area went this route. They developed land, started a mortgage company and had a major share in a real estate company. During the last major recession, the land development and the home building companies went bankrupt. The mortgage company was sold to another builder. The real estate company survives only as a shell of its former self. It can be a risky business.

Horizontal diversification

Horizontal diversification uses the same skills as the primary business, but expands the market to other consumers. These include: remodelling, light commercial construction and renovation, rental property construction, and by diversifying your price range to appeal to different markets. There is a higher probability of success here, since many of the skills needed in one business are transferrable to the other. In addition, these businesses can be counter cyclical. When interest rates go up and prospective customers put off buying a new home, they often remodel their old one instead. Apartment rentals produce income during periods of high or low interest rates.

By being able to shift personnel from one business to another, you can preserve key people when times are tough. This is a great strategy for the smaller builder, who can shift easily from remodelling to new construction. If you have cash reserves, it makes more sense to keep crews busy by building rental or commercial properties during down times, rather than buying down interest rates to keep building homes that no one is buying.

The major builder I mentioned above, managed to survive primarily because it built and managed rental properties during the good times. During the bad times, it fell back on the cash flow these rentals generated. If you have cash available during a downturn, it gives you the opportunity to buy land and buildings below market cost. This generates additional profit during the upturn, and can give you a lower competitive cost basis.

Geographic diversification

Sometimes, economic downturns are regional, not national. By diversifying geographically, you can minimize a local downturn. Secondly, you are using the same skills you used in the first market. There are several dangers. First, even though you understand the building business, you may lack a knowledge of the new local market. Business knowledge and market knowledge are two different things. As a result, you may not build in the best locations, or build a product suited for the local buyers. Second, you have added an additional management headache. If you think your business is difficult to manage now, try adding a new location several hundred or several thousand miles away. Third, you are still at risk during a national downturn.

Now What?

Diversifying into other businesses

There may be other income possibilities that take advantage of your skills and knowledge. The danger here is that you can lose your focus, especially if the businesses are unrelated. Concentrating on one business at a time is hard enough – concentrating on two can be impossible. If you have someone who can manage the second business for you then it becomes a diversification of investment. And that works.

Personal experience

From my personal experience, I've tried several diversification strategies. Some worked for me, and some didn't. During one downturn, we had the opportunity to renovate a historic building as an office condominium. Instead of being paid for our work, we received equity in the new building. The good news is that we made lots of money, at least on paper. The bad news is that we discovered that we hated being a landlord. Several times we've had the opportunity to develop small parcels of land. The key to land development is to structure the financing correctly, and to have cash reserves in order to take advantage of opportunities. In one case we subdivided a piece of land into 11 lots, and sold 3 lots (including the original house) for nearly the amount we paid for the entire parcel. With a little creative financing, we were able to walk away with very little debt, and even some cash-in-hand.

What works for you?

So what's the final answer? Just ask yourself these questions:
- Why am I diversifying? Am I successful in my present business?
- Do I have the skills it takes to succeed in the new business?
- Is the new business counter-cyclical to my present business?
- Will the new business spread my risk, or intensify it?
- Will the new business divert management focus, so that neither are managed well?
- Are the new opportunities commensurate with the risk?

If, after answering all those questions, you still feel you should diversify, then by all means go ahead. After all, it's your eggs, and your baskets. Just make sure that whatever you do, you watch the baskets.

Now What?

Who's Killing Your Profits?

You just got the job cost report back on your latest sale, and it looks more like a murder mystery than an expense statement. The profits you were expecting seem to have vanished into thin air. What went wrong?

Finding the answer is a little like solving a murder – you round up the usual suspects, you look for clues, and you try to eliminate the bad habits that lead to profit loss. One thing you shouldn't do is blame your competitors and their lower prices. If you're doing your job and looking for ways to improve profits every step of the way, it's the competition that will be worried, not you. These are the suspects you should investigate:

Estimating
Are your estimates accurate and complete? Do they include a miscellaneous category for the things that unexpectedly happen? Or do you indulge in wishful-thinking estimating in order to get the job?

Design
Are your home designs cost-effective and full of the "wow" factors that buyers fall in love with? Or are you spending too much for luxury materials to compensate for ho-hum design?

Sales and marketing
Do you lack a strong message in your marketing materials? Are you spending too little? Are sales suffering? Are you giving away too much in the price to close the sale?

Construction overruns and delays
If you're getting surprises from your subcontractors, then you need to take another look at your contracts. Also, every day you delay costs you extra in things like workers' pay and your loan interest, and that eats into your profits.

Overhead

Are you spending too much on overhead in relation to sales? Are you overstaffed? Can you reduce overhead by outsourcing?

Money management

Unless you have a good financial control system, you may be killing your profits and not even know you're doing it. You should have a job cost budget for each project, and get monthly variance reports on all items. The culprits will stand out like a sore thumb. You should also do a monthly ratio analysis comparing this month to last month and to year-to-date. That way, when things go wrong, you can detect them before the profit dies.

Leadership

Ultimately, the responsibility for profits rests on management itself. You have to create profit sensitivity at every level of your organization. If you don't pay attention, neither will anyone else.

Profits are a sought-after prize. They require constant care and attention, or they'll vanish. And their demise is rarely due to natural causes. You may find that the profits died from a conspiracy of mediocrity, poor sales, sloppy estimating, uncontrolled overhead, or lackluster design. But put on your detective cap, find out what happened to the profits, and do something about it. Otherwise you'll soon be asking, "Who killed the company?"

Diagnosing Your Business

Before you can solve a problem, you have to understand what the problem is. Below are 30 common problems faced by builders. They are divided into six functional areas. Review all of these issues, and check all those that you think could use improvement in your company. This becomes the basis for your Management Action Plan (MAP).

FINANCIAL CONTROL
❏ 1. Inaccurate and inefficient estimating procedures
❏ 2. Lack of operating budget and cost controls
❏ 3. Poor capitalization
❏ 4. Low (or unknown) profit margin
❏ 5. Poor purchasing controls

PRODUCT DESIGN
❏ 6. Product lacks pizzazz – insufficient market appeal
❏ 7. Product is expensive to build. Too complicated
❏ 8. No design/build capability. Inability to customize existing designs
❏ 9. Lack of separation and identity in marketplace. "Me too" designs
❏ 10. Failure to introduce new products, features, or ideas

SALES AND MARKETING
❏ 11. Ineffective marketing strategy
❏ 12. Lack of strong, consistent marketing message
❏ 13. Inadequate marketing materials (brochures, ads, logo, etc.)
❏ 14. Low referral rate from previous clients, Realtors, designers, and other professionals
❏ 15. Low closing rate with prospective clients

CUSTOMER SERVICE
❏ 16. Inadequate customer service program
❏ 17. Houses not completely ready at final walk-though
❏ 18. Client specification decisions not made in a timely manner

□ 19. Unrealistic quality expectations by clients
□ 20. High service warranty costs

CONSTRUCTION
□ 21. Lack of skilled craftsmen, reliable subcontractors
□ 22. Inadequate specifications and contracts with subcontractors
□ 23. Frequent scheduling delays
□ 24. Quality control problems
□ 25. Lack of timely response to material and manpower needs

LEADERSHIP
□ 26. Inadequate business plan
□ 27. Personnel problems – high turnover, poor productivity
□ 28. Inefficient procedures – scheduling, payroll, and paperwork
□ 29. Lack of skill or comfort negotiating with subs and clients
□ 30. Lack of vision and focus

PROBLEM PRIORITIES

After you have selected all those areas that could stand improvement, then select the three issues where you feel your company is the strongest, and three areas where you feel your company is the weakest. Select areas that you feel would have the greatest positive impact in your company.

THREE GREATEST STRENGTHS
1. _____
2. _____
3. _____

THREE BIGGEST PROBLEMS
1. _____
2. _____
3. _____

Now go through the problem-solving process for each of these three problems. Set deadlines for resolving the problems and assign responsibility and resources. Then repeat for the next set of three problems.

Now What?   161

The Economics of Education

At the heart of every personal computer is a small chunk of silicon called the microprocessor. The raw materials it contains are worth a few pennies, but the chip itself can be worth hundreds of dollars. The difference between the raw materials and the finished product is "information." It's what the manufacturer does with the materials, not the materials themselves, that create the value.

The same is true in homebuilding. The difference between a home that people want to live in, and a dog that's a drag on the market is information: client information, design information, construction information, process information. The difference between a company that is making money hand over fist and one that's hemorrhaging red ink is management information.

Like it or not, builders are in the information business. What your customers are paying for is not materials and labor, but the intelligence with which those materials and labor are used and assembled. The sooner builders realize this, the sooner they can begin to focus on the aspects of their business that really matter. Increased information leads to increased professionalism, productivity, motivation, and profit orientation. Occasionally it leads to break through thinking and big money-making ideas.

How do you increase information?

The primary way builders increase the level of information within their company is through education, both for themselves and their staff. They can acquire education in two ways – through seminars and conference, and through individual learning, including reading and training. Both are important tools, and can have an impact on profits far beyond their costs.

Seminars and conferences

When was the last time your whole team went to a seminar together to get charged up and acquire new ideas? It's not enough for the owner/ builder to attend. He can't disseminate the information and experience to his staff by osmosis. In addition, when staff share a common experience, it improves communication and bonding between them.

Some of the best experiences available are through the Customer Builder Symposium sponsored by NAHB, the Builder University tours, the TeamBuilder Conference and the Custom Home show sponsored by Hanley-Wood, regional shows such as PCBC and the Southern Building Conference, and the seminars provided though your local Home Builder Associations.

Company based education

Once you've taken advantage of the educational opportunities out there, you then need to focus on specific company needs. Look and see what training is available through your local college or adult education program. These can include courses on specific computer applications, marketing, and customer service. You may want to create company-wide seminars and corporate retreats to focus on specific problems and foster team-building. Teach them yourself, or find someone to come in and provide an outside perspective on your goals and operations.

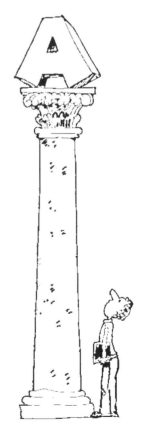

Self-directed learning

You need to make learning and self-improvement a corporate goal. Encourage your staff to read, take classes, and attend lectures. After all, continuous learning requires continuous effort. To do that you need to set an example. You could build a company library – books that provide technical expertise, as well as general industry insight. If you find a book that you really like, have everyone in the company read it so that you can discuss how to implement the ideas.

If you want to keep growing in a changing environment, you and your staff have got to keep learning. It's as simple as that.

What's Your Exit Strategy?

O ne of the sad facts of life is that people get older, they slow down, and the business they built must be transferred to new management if it is to survive. Builders who anticipate the inevitable can maximize the value of their company when that time comes, and minimize the disruption in the transition process. Early in your career, your emphasis was "How do I make my business profitable?" When you begin to think about exit strategies, the emphasis is "How do I get these assets out of the company, either in cash, or as a revenue stream." These are different perspectives, leading to different business strategies.

What are you selling?

In order to sell a company, you first have to decide exactly what it is you're selling. A building business is a rather unique blend of service and manufacturing. Much of the actual work is performed by outside subcontractors. The most valuable asset of the company is often the management expertise of key personnel, which can disappear overnight if the company changes hands. Think of your building business as a machine – a money-making machine. Inside this machine are hard assets (cash, land, equipment, property), soft assets (management expertise, systems, personnel), and intangible assets (good will.) The value of the company is what someone is willing to pay for this money making machine, plus the value of the assets generated by the machine.

Some of the hard assets (land, portfolio property) can often be separated from the business and sold separately, or retained by the owner. So you have to decide what you will sell, how you will sell it, who you will sell it to, and what participation you will have (if any) in the future entity. You also have to decide how you will exit. The major strategies are to close down shop (liquidate assets), pass the torch to a new generation, sell to an outside builder, or sell to inside key personnel. All of these considerations become part of your exit strategy.

Passing the Torch

If you have a child who would like to take over the business when you retire, you may not have to sell at all. What you do have to work out,

164 **Now What?**

however, is how the business will continue to generate revenue for you after you retire. Any agreement between you and the next generation should spell out how much of the profits are earmarked for you, and over what period of time.

Don't pass it to someone who doesn't want it

Whatever you do, don't force someone to take over the business just to keep your family involvement. To be successful at the building business, you really have to love it. If their heart is elsewhere, let them follow their dream, just as you followed yours.

Selling Outside

You may be able to get a higher price for your company by selling the company outright. You can sell to a local competitor, to a regional or national builder, you can participate in a roll-up with other builders, or you can take your company public.

Another local builder

Local competitors may be interested in gaining market share by buying you out rather than continuing to fight with you. But working for a competitor (even a friendly one) can be very difficult after the transition. In selling to another local builder, make sure that your rights and your employees' rights are protected in writing. Don't assume good will is sufficient to carry you through.

Large regional or national builders

If you have sufficient sales volume ($15 million plus), you may attract the attention of a large regional or national builder who is looking to increase market share or enter a new market. The advantage of selling to a larger builder is that they have the capital and resources to aggressively grow the business, and to buy you out on an accelerated schedule. If they merge your old identity in with theirs, there is a loss of pride of ownership; however, you can console yourself every time you check your bank balance.

Going Public

This is the ultimate approach to enhancing the value of your company, but it's not for the faint of heart or the smaller player. Companies that have gone public successfully have often made their principals overnight multi-millionaires. In addition the principals can sell some of their shares without selling the entire company. If you have the sales volume, make sure you get good financial help in setting up your IPO.

Selling to key employees

In deciding to sell to key employees, you have to ask the following questions: Do they have the skills? Do they have the capital? And can you structure the deal in a way that will make it easy for them to make a successful transition?

Hopefully, your key personnel have learned to handle authority and executive decision making. If their skills are too limited or specialized, you either have to begin cross-training them or find the skills they need through hiring new personnel. If your employees haven't amassed sufficient capital to buy you out you can arrange for them to retain part of their profit sharing and bonus revenue in the company to create a gradual buyout fund.

Is there life after exit?

One of the greatest dangers of exiting a business you have built and managed is the feeling of loss of control and identity. Often a great part of their identity is tied up in the business, and when they leave it, they feel an empty void in their life. This is a dangerous time in the transition process. If you've passed the torch to a new generation, the temptation is to retake control or meddle in operations in order to feel important. Resist the temptation. Find a new challenge. Start a new business. Find a niche where you can contribute to your old company, without taking control again. Become a land developer. Develop a new product line. Volunteer your time to work that you feel is significant and uses your skills.

Just because you've exited your old business doesn't mean that you have to be put out to pasture. You probably have decades of highly productive and rewarding life left to live. And if you've exited your business successfully, you'll have the financial resources to live that life comfortably.

Now What?

Postscript

If you started at the beginning of the book, (like most people), you've just finished reading *Building with an Attitude.* Hopefully, you've developed some attitudes of your own. Like the attitude that the building business can be fun, if done right. And that it's even more fun, when it's done profitably. However, there are a lot of little things that can get in the way of the fun and profits.

Some of those things can be changed. If your procedures are either inadequate or overly complicated, change them and make your life easier. If your biggest problem is dealing with customers, improve your communication skills to eliminate unrealistic expectations. If you build a great house at a reasonable price but no one knows about it, change your marketing program. If your houses look like everyone else's, set yourself apart through better design and detail. Use technology wherever it promises to increase your productivity. Provide your employees the tools, training, and direction needed to do the kind of job you can be proud of.

Some things can be avoided. Develop a program for identifying problem clients and sending them to your competitors. Avoid the lure of new technology when it offers more complexity than you can deal with. Replace subs that are unreliable and inconsistent. Get rid of problem employees who drag down the morale and productivity of everyone else.

Some things simply need an attitude adjustment. Sure, it drives you crazy when buyers change their mind after you've ordered the materials (or even installed them). But as long as there's a big enough check attached to that change order, it's an aggravation you can live with. Sure, it takes more work and thought to offer mass customization of your existing plans. But the end result is a house that makes the client happier, and you more profitable.

This is a great time to be a builder. Buyers have never had more disposable income, or greater sophistication about design and materials. But it's also a time of challenge. The industry is changing rapidly. The builders who survive and thrive over the coming years will be the ones who have examined their business and created an attitude of fun, excellence, and profits. We hope to see you there.

About the Authors

Al Trellis

Before becoming a consultant and speaker, Al Trellis was a custom builder in Columbia, Maryland constructing approximately ten to twelve homes per year in the suburban Maryland area. Alan is the author of eight books on residential construction, including *The Road to Success is Always Under Construction*, and writes a monthly column for Builder Magazine, entitled "Ask Al". In 1991 he founded the Home Builders Network, which provides consulting and information for small volume builders and the home building industry. A member of the NAHB Custom Builder Committee for the six years ending in 1994, Al helped create the NAHB Custom Builder Symposium and chaired the event for its first five years. A frequent speaker at national and local seminars and workshops, Al has been consistently rated as one of the country's leading speakers at the NAHB National Convention, Custom Builder Symposium, and over eighty state and local associations.

Paul Sharp

Paul Sharp is a writer and marketing consultant, with over 20 years experience developing marketing programs. He is a co-founder of Home Builders Network, and provides marketing and management services for home builders as well as building industry manufacturers and suppliers. He is the co-author of the book *The Road to Success is Always Under Construction*, and the popular seminar *program Who Killed the Profits?*

Home Builders Network
205 E. Ridgeville Blvd., Suite C, Mt. Airy, MD 21771
1-800-823-4344, Fax 301-829-8907
www.HBNnet.com   Mail@HBNnet.com